CW00819365

THE CHRONICLES
OF DON'T
BE SO RIDICULOUS VALLEY

First edition published 2019

Published by
London Street Books

LONDON STREET
BOOKS.COM

In association with
Mango Books

ISBN: 978-1-911273-83-7

www.LondonStreetBooks.com

THE CHRONICLES OF DON'T BE SO RIDICULOUS VALLEY

By Mike Batt

Illustrated by John Gosler
and others

THE CHRONICLES
OF DON'T
BE SO RIDICULOUS
VALLEY

Chapter One: Once A Slug...

Once (not as far back as the Olden Days, but fairly far back, somewhere between the Olden Days and last week), there was a medium-sized slug called Ergo. He had some mates. The mates were slugs, too, and also medium-sized. They all lived in a very unusual place called Don't Be So Ridiculous Valley. The valley was called Don't Be So Ridiculous Valley because it was actually a hill, and hills go upwards whereas valleys go downwards and along. Some people might tell you that hills go downwards, but they are pessimists. Hills go upwards. Valleys go downwards, and even then only in the nicest possible way.

On Friday evenings, if it was cool, they would slip quietly down to the orchard to wait for the fish and chips to fall contentedly from the branches. Some of the more deep-thinking slugs thought that the mummies and daddies put the fish and chips up there in the middle of the night, but most of them believed that they just grew there, not even by magic (for if a thing is true it is just true, and not magic) and they were the ones who were right.

"Slugs, that's what we are," they said, fairly often. And frankly, they were right about that. Not horrible black slugs like the ones you slip on in the garden, but silvery-glitter slugs with bright orange slimy bits underneath, and small, round, smiley, cheeky faces.

They often found it hard to get up in the morning. Perhaps it was because they had no legs. Or perhaps it was because they never went to bed. Ergo had a strong wish to do something in life other than wait for the fish and chips to fall from the trees. Everything seemed too safe. He had often thought about running away from home – but once again, not having legs made this unlikely. His life was certainly pleasant, but there seemed such little excitement and adventure. He did have an old gramophone with some George Formby records, but the frequent moments of emotional uplift afforded by these only made him yearn all the more for the unknown glories which he knew came only to those who made the effort to break away from the daily safety of being Normal.

"Once a slug, always a slug," said Ergo, with chilling accuracy. He carefully inserted a stick of chewing gum into his small and not particularly interesting mouth and slopped wearily off into the fog. But this time, instead of slopping off back round to his mother's house, where he lived, he just kept right on slopping. He hadn't decided in a real, executive decision to keep on going, he just went. And went. And when he'd nearly finished going he went even a bit further.

It was a dull, foggy morning (otherwise there wouldn't have been any fog for Ergo to slop off into just now), but it was dull in a fairly bright sort of way. The sort of way that means you can only just see your hand in front of your face (if you have hands, and if one of them is in front of your face, which was not the case) – but bright, so that there was a broad glare right across his field of vision, or vision of field, I should really say, since it was indeed a field that Ergo had vision of – or didn't, really, if you see what I mean.

The morning dew hung happily on the grass around him, waiting for something to happen. The thing that happened was that the dew dried up and ceased to exist. Ergo was thinking about this rather harsh fact of life as he nosed his way ever onwards into the unknown. Just then, he ran out of chewing gum.

"Oh dear," thought Ergo, for he was a bright and perceptive slug, "I seem to have run out of chewing gum."

Nige and Dotty's Tree house

In their tree house some miles away and not even close to Don't Be So Ridiculous Valley, the Farnsbarneses were just getting up and doing their exercises. Dotty Farnsbarnes and her husband, Mr Farnsbarnes, were unlike all the other little fairy folk, because they had bought themselves a matching pair of combat helicopters which they kept in a large disused Owl-hole, which was of course simultaneously occupied by a Large Disused Owl.

Dotty's helicopter was pink until midday, and light blue with a dark blue stripe after lunch (on Mondays, Wednesdays and Fridays), and Mr Farnsbarnes' was light blue with a dark blue stripe in the mornings and pink after lunch. This helped them to tell the difference between the two helicopters, which were, in every other respect, identical. On Tuesdays, Thursdays and weekends the rules were reversed, and Dotty's was light blue before lunch and pink after lunch. This caused a certain amount of confusion, which they solved either by only ever using one helicopter at a time, or by not minding if one of them used the other's helicopter by mistake.

Over breakfast, Dotty and Mr Farnsbarnes made their plans for the day, which they decided would involve a trip to the small village shopping area some distance from their own area of woodland bits and bobs called Woodland Land, out across the next lump of countryside which was called I Thought I Told You Not To Be So Ridiculous Valley, and which was unlike Don't Be So Ridiculous Valley in that it was a real valley which went downwards and along, and it did it in a very nice way indeed. It was beautiful countryside, of the sort that Mr Farnsbarnes called "jolly pretty".

There had been a time – when they were both young – when Mr Farnsbarnes had thought that his wife, Dotty, was jolly pretty, but now she was only a bit pretty, but also a tiny bit ugly. However, as he reminded himself (for he was an optimist), she was only a very little tiny bit ugly and still quite a big bit pretty. This was only fair, because Mr Farnsbarnes was also getting older every day and, it had to be admitted, was very slightly less handsome than he had been as a young man fairy. Thankfully, Dotty had not noticed this, as she was even more of an optimist than Mr Farnsbarnes – or maybe she had noticed it, but didn't mind.

After bidding the Large Disused Owl a very good morning, they carefully selected Dotty's helicopter using a calendar, a clock and a colour chart, filled its fuel tank full of tea (containing a ratio of two sugars to the Woodland litre), and took off into the morning mist, the pinkness of the helicopter glinting in the sunshine, reminding them that it must be Monday, Wednesday or Friday.

"The helicopter seems to be turning blue," said Mr Farnsbarnes.

"Gosh, is that the time!" said Dotty, looking at the colour chart on the wall, and reaching out for a large basket of pigeon's milk and a bag of onions which they had brought along for their mid-morning snack. Dotty, who was driving the helicopter, let go of the controls for a moment as she leant over to get the bag, and it lurched violently to the left. Luckily, a bag of onions and pigeon's milk lurching violently to the left is not dangerous. If it had been the helicopter which had lurched violently, it could have been very nasty indeed.

"Let's land – steering and eating at the same time is all rather difficult," said Dotty, wisely.

She skilfully brought the flying machine down in the middle of a field, where she could see enough through the mist to enable her to land smoothly. The morning dew had recently dried, which was odd, because the mist was still floating above the field in its usual soft, light blue way.

"Great to be alive, eh, Dotty!" enthused Mr Farnsbarnes, jumping down from the helicopter and looking around him. This started him off thinking, for he was a thinking sort of fairy – indeed an inventor of some importance to the local community (at least in his own estimation, and Dotty's, or so she said). He was thinking about the meaning of life, the nature of a superior being if indeed there was one – which he doubted – and about whether there might be a way to peel onions without your eyes watering. He was pretty sure he had the answers to the first two questions – which weren't really questions, more like topics for discussion – but was stumped about the third problem. Maybe if you were under water, or just your arms were, you could peel onions without the smelly onion vapour escaping up into your eyes. Goggles would be awkward, and difficult for the cook if he or she would soon have to sit down to dinner with guests, looking nice, and without make-up being smudged. Of course, he didn't use make-up, but Dotty did, just like all fairies who are just a tiny weeny bit ugly but not very.

"What are you thinking about, my Darling?" asked Dot, breaking his chain of thought and rather irritating him. She was always doing it, but he had grown tolerant of it. Who knows how many inventions she had denied to the world by breaking his concentration in this way? Probably heaps. It was a good job there were other inventors of nearly his calibre in the world, he thought, rather generously.

"Nothing you would understand, my dear little wife-in-a-million," he replied. Dotty blushed. She spread out a blanket on the ground and slit open the bag with a penknife with lots of gadgets, like a Swiss Army knife but not quite as good because it didn't have a thing for getting stones out of horses' hooves. This didn't matter because there were no horses. Or if there were, they had never seen one yet.

Dotty didn't mind her husband talking down to her in this patronising way. She rather liked it. It made her feel small and slightly inferior (which was far from the truth, she had a Woodland PhD in Nuclear Physics, Flower Arranging and Cake Decorating), and it helped her to love him as much as she did

– which was a lot – as it enabled her to look up to him.

She got out two onions, polished one on the front of her shirt and bowled it, overarm with a slight top-spin, to her lovely husband, with a warm smile.

"Here you are, my husband-for-ever-and-ever," she purred, in her sweet little voice and fairy accent. Her accent was a little like an Australian accent with a hint of something like Russian around the vowels. But despite – or possibly because of – these two things, it was a charming speaking voice.

"Fog's clearing," observed Mr Farnsbarnes.

"You're not wrong even a little tiny bit" agreed Dot, happily. She bit into her raw onion with a loud but feminine crunch, and chewed thoughtfully. To have had some children would have been nice, she thought. Still, she had old Farnsey. And the Large Disused Owl. "Lucky, lucky, lucky me," she thought. She bit the onion again. Some people didn't have enough to eat. Some people didn't even have houses, but she had Nigel Farnsbarnes, a sister called Elsie, a half share in two helicopters, a doctorate, an owl, a tree house, and lots of other things. Phew!

They were both stretching out on the blanket, feeling happy and munching on their onions, when Nigel's hair burst into flames.

"Whaaaaaarrrrrrrrrrr!" said Nigel, in a surprised and pained manner, which was not a planned thing, more an instant reaction to the searing pain that ripped across his scalp.

In a flash, Dotty ran over to the helicopter and turned on the rotor blades, hoping that the fire would be blown out, but of course this just fanned the flames even higher.

"Whaaaaaarrrrr and yet twice and thrice Whaaaaaaar!!!" added Nigel.

Just then, Ergo, who had been making his way peacefully through the field, having noticed the Farnsbarneses enjoying their picnic, leapt onto the blanket, grabbed the pigeon's milk with one of his slimy knobbly bits that slugs have instead of hands, and emptied the entire basket of it (2.4 Woodland litres) over the roaring flames on Nigel's head, which by now were several Woodland feet high, and not very funny at all for poor old Nige.

The fire went out instantly, but the top of Nigel's head continued to smoulder and smoke, giving off a column of black fumes, the smell of which which reminded Ergo of barbecued pine nuts.

"Oh, thank you, thank you!" yelled Dotty, rushing over to Nigel, who was rolling around on the ground, holding his head. He was still in considerably more than a medium amount of pain.

"What happened?" asked Nigel.

"Your hair just... er, caught fire, darling husband-of-my-dreams," said Dotty.

"I know, but why?"

"Why does the river flow to the sea? Why does the wind whisper in the night? What is Life? How many inches in a nautical mile?" said Dotty, a trifle flippantly. The only thing she cared about was that he was safe. Her Nigel, safe and sound, if a trifle smoky around the scalp.

"No, I insist on knowing," raged Nigel Farnsbarnes, still rolling about in pain.

He suddenly remembered Ergo.

"Oh – er, thanks for – er, extinguishing me with the pigeon's milk, mate," he said, a little inadequately.

"It was the least I could do," said Ergo.

"Why didn't you do more then?" asked Mr Farnsbarnes jokingly, as he winced with pain, and held his head with both hands.

"Well, it was the least and the most I could do," explained Ergo, not seeing the joke. "In that sense, it was the only thing to do."

"Do you mean to say that the only available thing to do when you see a man with his hair on fire is to throw a basket of pigeon's milk on it? I think not!" reasoned Mr Farnsbarnes, who always liked a stimulating argument. "What if there wasn't any pigeon's milk, but there was a fire extinguisher?"

"Come on, Mr Farnsbarnes," interrupted Dotty, "this is a silly argument."

"Let me introduce myself," said Mr Farnsbarnes, to Ergo. "I'm Nigel Farnsbarnes – inventor, man of letters... oh, and quite a good gardener, and this is my wife, Dotty, who is, well, wife of me, the inventor and so on. Pleased to meet you. And you are...?"

He left that sort of inquisitive pause that people leave when they are inviting you to finish the sentence. Ergo wondered why he didn't just say "What is your name?" but he didn't.

"Ergo. A slug of medium size, from Don't Be So Ridiculous Valley," offered Ergo.

"Well, slug or not, you certainly saved my hair from not being extinguished!" said Nigel, sounding like an idiot, but not knowing what else to say.

"That's not wrong, and no mistake," said Dot.

"Glad to have been of service," said Ergo.

"Why do you think my hair burst into flames?" asked Mr Farnsbarnes.

"I don't know. We don't get much spontaneous combustion of the scalp around here," said Ergo.

"I know, I live here, too. Well, not here, exactly, just over that big hill and round through the big woods..." Nigel's voice trailed off as he realised that Ergo probably wouldn't be interested in exactly where he lived.

"Any danger of me coming for a ride in your flying machine?" asked Ergo.

"It's the least we can do!" said Nigel.

"Why don't you do more then?!" quipped Ergo, who had got the joke after all.

The three friends took off in the helicopter and rose up over I Thought I Told You Not To Be So Ridiculous Valley.

As the journey continued, the Farnsbarneses discovered that Ergo was actually the slug equivalent of a great bloke. Ergo began to tell them funny stories of life in Don't Be So Ridiculous Valley, and all about his mates in the orchard, eating their fish and chips every Friday night.

"He's a really nice chap, this slug," said Mr Farnsbarnes as he began to blow softly on a mouth organ which had been lying on the floor, having fallen out of Dotty's handbag. "Pass me an onion, Dot!"

Dotty reached over from the helicopter controls and passed him another large white onion, and Mr Farnsbarnes began to munch hungrily on it, between little tuneful blows and sucks on the mouth organ.

"Where are we going?" said Ergo.

"Oh, I'm sorry," said Dotty. We're only going back to our house. It's quite boring, really."

"Not at all," replied Ergo, "I'm sure it's very interesting. Could I come with you? You see I'm looking for adventure and this is the most exciting thing I've ever done."

The Farnsbarneses told Ergo he would be most welcome to return home with them, and so he sat up in the co-pilot's seat and watched the trees flashing past beneath them as they flew. Soon, they arrived at the Farnsbarnes' tree residence, where they landed. Ergo was introduced to the Large Disused Owl, who had been woken up by the noise of the rotor blades and was a little bit grumpy.

Chapter Two: Ergo's Army

A few days later, Ergo and Dotty were having a gossip in the kitchen. Ergo told Dotty a joke about two pigs and a gravy boat.

"Don't mention pigs to me,"groaned Dot, "my brother was killed by one of the evil pigfrog warriors who live in Everywhere Else and come out every December. They are so horrid, I can hardly speak."

Ergo was shocked. The hairy bits under his slimy bits stood on end.

"Sounds ghastly," he sympathised. "What exactly is a pigfrog, and why do they only come out in December?"

"They're seasonal," replied Dotty importantly, as if that explained everything.

"Oh," said Ergo. "So we'd better not go to Everywhere Else in December, then."

Which they didn't.

Actually, they did (I was lying about that). Later in the story, when we get to the bit about the Wars between the slugs and the pigfrogs, you'll see what I mean. Pigfrogs were nasty pieces of work. The hills, before they ever became alive with music, were infested with pigfrogs, back in caveman days. They would creep up behind people and jump on them from a great height, using their enormous pink hind legs to launch the entire bulk of their sweaty, fleshy pink bodies skywards, then plummeting down vertically onto their victims. To be landed on by a pigfrog was certain death, and what is more, very irritating indeed. The pigfrog warriors gave out a fierce scream as their battle cry.

LEGS STRAIGHT ON JUMP UP

LEGS SPLAY ON DOWNWARD MOTION FOR SUPERIOR SQUASHING

They dribbled on people, too. Even the friendly ones were horrible (and there weren't any). Now, after the purge of Slunder (a secret story only told to gold subscribers of the Don't Be So Ridiculous Valley annual), they had retreated from the borders of I Thought I Told You Not To Be So Ridiculous Valley and That's Better Valley and had hidden in the caves of Everywhere Else, coming out every December, mainly for the purpose of spoiling Christmas. Which they didn't. Well, OK then, they did. Let's be honest.

"Do you mean that you can quite literally be strolling along on the 30th of November in Everywhere Else, minding your own business, and suddenly nothing happens; yet on the first of December, you'll be doing the same thing and you suddenly cease to exist because some pigfrog you've never even met has crept up behind you and changed your shape from lumpy to flat?"

"Yes, that's the sort of thing, Ergo," said Dotty.

"Flipping Heck!" exclaimed Ergo. "That's not very fair! I don't think it should be allowed."

"Life wasn't meant to be fair," said Mr F. "Look at me; I have to play the harmonica while Dotty only has to do the housework."

"I'm going to do something about it!" said Ergo, with new anger.

"No, really, it's fine," said Mr F, "I'm quite happy playing the harmonica, and the housework does Dotty good."

"No, not that," replied Ergo, frustratedly. "I mean the pigfrogs. I'll recruit an army and we'll march on them and destroy them. We'll rid this peaceful land of the scourge of these evil monsters once and for all."

Mr F was, by now, playing a stirring, patriotic piece on the harmonica, and Dotty was wiping a little tear from his cheek. Mr F had a highly-developed sense of occasion and was prone to these involuntary displays of raw emotion.

"...so that little children will sleep easily in their cots and old people can live in peace and die at their leisure, or preferably even later," continued Ergo.

By now he was red in the face, and looking up into the sky (through the kitchen window) with fierce eyes and a noble expression.

⁓⁓

The next morning, the soft smell of breakfast woodsmoke hung in the air.

Ergo galvanised himself into action. In the Farnsbarnes' household, Euphoria had broken out.

"Catch Euphoria and chain her to the sink again, will you, Mr F?" shouted Dotty from upstairs, where she was doing her make-up.

"Yes, Dear," said her husband, shooing the cat back to its basket with one of Dotty's copper-bottomed frying pans.

"There's a wonderful smell hanging in the air," said Ergo. "What exactly is it?"

Mr F reached for the spray and looked at the label.

"Let me see now... BREAKFAST WOODSMOKE... it's a new one. We'd been getting a little tired of Cheese and Onion – it gets in your clothes and hair and you just can't get rid of it."

Reaching for Dotty's pretty little Woodlands Telephone Service handset, Ergo punched in four digits and waited, listening to the soft burr of the ringing tone at the other end.

"Hello," said Ergo's mother.

"Mum!" shouted Ergo. "It's me!"

"Well, blow me down – if I wasn't already down – what with being a slug and all!" exclaimed his mother, in amazement.

"No time for jokes, Mum, this is important," interrupted Ergo. "Look, I'm sorry I disappeared, and I'll explain later. Right now I'm urgently trying to recruit a mighty army, so I won't pass the time of day, if you don't mind. Can you run down the road (in a manner of speaking) and get Sodge to come to the phone. It's really, really important, Mum."

His mother left the phone dangling as she raced down to Sodge's house. Sodge was Ergo's best mate. They had been in some real scrapes together, or at least pretended they had, for not much actually happened in Don't Be So Ridiculous Valley.

"Sodge, Sodge, come quickly, it's Ergo on the blower!" shouted Ergo's mum, as she bashed on the little wooden door.

"OK Mrs E!" answered Sodge. (Parents were always addressed by the initial letter of their first-born child). Sodge was soon at the telephone, greeting his old pal.

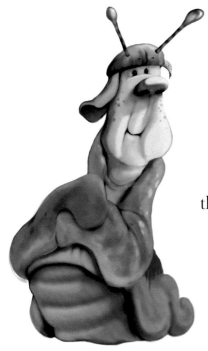

"Look, Sodge, get your sweet little slimy bits down here as fast as you can," urged Ergo, not saying where he was, "I'll explain later."

"Or maybe I ought to explain now. It's just that there are these horrible things called pigfrogs and they creep up behind you and jump on you in December, and you die. And they dribble a lot, and Dotty's told me all about them, and it's got to stop, if you see what I mean."

"I know exactly what you mean!" said Sodge. "I'm your slug! You can count on me. Shall I get the others?"

"Yes, please, Sodge. I'll get Dotty and Mr F to come over in the helicopters. Can you find any nasty, vicious weapons to bring? You know the sort of thing."

"Trouble is, we won't be much use against these pigfrog efforts, what with not being able to walk for a start," offered Sodge.

"Good point, Sodge. I'll have to think about that one." Ergo wasn't unduly worried. This was an adventure, and he was sure it would have a happy ending.

"One thing, Sodge. Could you please bring my gramophone and my George Formby records?"

※

Mr Farnsbarnes emerged from his workshop with a bewildered look on his face. He was an excellent inventor and was always tinkering with little gadgets like delay mechanisms for Helicopter Colour Drift Syndrome, underwater onion peelers and cat detectors. The cat detectors never caught on because most people can detect cats anyway.

The reason for the look of bewilderment was that he had been designing a prototype set of Slug Wheels for Ergo. They would be like a cross between an invalid carriage and a skateboard, but he was stuck on the power source. He had decided that Lemonade power would be too expensive, and petrol was too boring. Electricity was too obvious, and gas was, well, too gassy. Suddenly, he had a great idea.

"I've got a great idea!" he said.

Onion Power was his idea. Why hadn't he thought of it before? Here's how it worked! A small person or woodland animal would sit at the back of the little tray upon which the occupant slug would lie. The person or woodland animal would eat onions, taken from a trolley attached to the back of the slug tray, and would breathe into a sensitised wind-sock linked to a power transformer which would burn the onion gas, and a gear system which would then drive the vehicle along. The slug could steer and control the power. It was quite brilliant. Nothing could go wrong! He began building the new system immediately, and about two pages later was ready to demonstrate the technology to Ergo and the bizarre crew of slug comrades who by now were disporting themselves around the tree in which the Farnsbarneses lived.

Nige was pleased with himself.

"Ergo! Listen, Mate," he began, "I'm so flipping enormously pleased with myself I can't begin to tell you!"

He stood the slugs (in a manner of speaking) in a horseshoe shape, and pulled The Wheels out into the centre of the group. They were as I described before – a skateboard, at the back of which sat a small, bored-looking woodland creature called Kevin. It perched on a sort of tennis umpire's stool. A trolley of onions was attached at the rear.

"This," Mr F explained, "is the historic moment when I reveal to you the means by which you will transcend an entire evolutionary stage! I present to you the invention by which I hope I shall be remembered when I'm dead, or hopefully even earlier: Nige's Wheels!" he announced.

"Hop in, Ergo!"

Ergo mounted (in a manner of speaking) the slug tray part of the apparatus.

"Press the green button, to start the power!" urged Nige.

Ergo did, using a slimy bit. A small green light shone up into the woodland creature's eyes.

The woodland creature, on cue, took a healthy bite from one of the onions and breathed out demonstratively into the windsock. Loud orchestral music began, and the engines kicked into action.

"Ooh!" said the slugs on the left.

"Aah!" said the slugs on the right.

The next days were spent recruiting and equipping the slug force. Ergo's Army was now several hundred strong, and growing. He had almost run out of slugs to recruit, and was trying to decide how many extra fighting bodies he would need when Dotty came rushing into the room waving a telegram from her little sister Elsie, or Else, as she was called. Little Else was coming to stay. Hip, Hip, Hooray!

"Ergo, would you be a dear and go with Nige to pick up Little Else from the station?" said Dot.

"Well I suppose I can continue my plan to rid the world of evil pigfrogs when I get back," said Ergo, sarcastically. "Put the kettle on, Dotty."

He and Nigel got into the correct helicopter, which was now pink (for it was after lunch on a Wednesday), and took off, arriving at the station just in time to see the little train pulling into the station.

"Little Else!" shouted Nige, as a small, rather attractive fairy in a tweed jacket got out of the train.

"I'm Ergo" said Ergo, accurately.

"You're probably right," said Elsie. She smiled. "Sounds like Latin," she added.

"I can't carry your bags because I'm only a slug," apologised Ergo.

They walked back to the helicopter. On the way home, Little Else explained that she had come so that she could look after Chez Farnsbarnes while everybody was out conquering the pigfrogs, or whatever. Ergo was delighted.

"That means Dotty and Nige are coming with us!" he deduced.

That evening, they held a council of war. After some discussion, it was decided that more intelligence was needed. Not enough was known about the enemy. Dotty had explained that the pigfrogs were able to creep up on people very quietly before letting out that horrible scream – "a scream that the victim would only hear the first half of," as Dot said.

"Don't end a sentence with a preposition," said Nigel, tetchily.

"A pigfrog is about twice the size of a slug, and twenty times meaner," said Dotty.

"Slugs aren't mean at all," said Sodge.

"What is all this leading to?" said Dotty.

"Please don't end sentences with prepositions!" said Nigel, in an unusual show of anger. He burst into tears.

"The nasty thing about pigfrogs is that they don't really need to jump on people at all," Dotty continued. "They don't eat you or anything. It's not as if they needed the meat. They only do it for fun."

"Fun?" bellowed Ergo. "For flipping fun! Ooh, I can't tell you how cross I'm getting."

It was decided that an advance party would make a trip out to Everywhere Else, crossing the Mauve and Avocado Mountains at the most cold and difficult point, the Avocado Basin. This would be far more fun than going by Woodland Railway, which was free, and only took forty-five minutes. If you went the easy way, there wasn't such a sense of achievement at the end, and you didn't get to cook your food on a little fire and sing rude songs, Ergo had said.

Ergo looked across the room. Something about the way Little Else was smiling, something in her manner, had caused him to stop for a minute. Could it be that he was falling in love? Oh, no! But, yes, he did seem to be unusually excited by the soft, undulating tone of her voice and the way she stood with her hands on her cute little hips.

"Oh, no!" thought Ergo. Not a good thing! What with her being a real live girl-type fairy person, and him only being a slug. Fat chance of her feeling the same! And even then, what an annoying and distracting thing to happen on the eve of the wars between the slugs and the pigfrogs! There they'd all be, off up the mountains with war in their souls, and what would Ergo be doing?

Thinking of Little Else. Not good. He would try to put it out of his mind. Ignore it. Forget about it.

"Forget about what?" he thought. Good, it had worked.

He surveyed the motley array of recruits which were spread out before him. They were good types, all of them. By now, his slug Elite Corps had been augmented by a good few humanoid-types, either fairies or gnomes. And there were one or two travelling accountants, bored with their usual profession and seeking a little excitement. These were gnome-folk who wandered around, making their homes among whomever it was who would hire them to count their money. They were called gnome-adds.

As for the slugs themselves, there was old Erk, the brave campaigner who had beaten off eleven enemy single-handedly in the Greenfly Wars. "It was nothing," he would say. Nobody disagreed. Then there was Fudgebrother The Younger, an artist by profession, who had been one of the earliest to respond to the call. Then came Froon, the library monitor; Slarjk, the flower-cutter; Spittoon, the schoolmaster, and Sir John Marvellousbloke, the name-giver. It was he who thought up everyone's name. Not always a popular slug. A little selfish. But brave.

Ergo had to admit, they were all brave and true.

Chapter Three: The Magnificent Thirty-Five

Now that Mr Farnsbarnes (as I shall still sometimes call him) had been able to go into full production with his newly-patented Wheels, the entire slug army was kitted out with a set each; a squirreloid or other friendly member of the woodland underclass sat at the rear of each machine, ready to respond to the power button.

Nige had fine-tuned the machines in accordance with Ergo and Sodge's instructions, so that they were now very quiet indeed (no engine noise, to speak of, and no orchestral music) and there was a vast array of different variations across the front. Weapons, telescopes, umbrellas, fondue sets, all sorts of things. Nige was to receive a small design credit and a royalty on each set made. This would be calculated by the gnome-adds and paid quarterly.

The next day, thirty-five of the toughest slugs set out on the reconnaissance expedition. They left at the crack of dawn, their progress over the rough ground made easier by the fitting of rough-ground tyres to their wheels. Ergo could not help feeling a flash of excitement in the pit of his digestive tract. This was the real thing. The day they had trained so hard for. His soldiers looked the part, at least. They bristled with weapons, flags and equipment, all of which was attached to the "handlebars" at the front, just above the head. Many also wore helmets made of leather and wood. Even the woodland creatures were kitted out in armoured vests and helmets, giving them the appearance of gladiators riding strange chariots. A separate sled carried the gramophone, which Nigel Farnsbarnes had slung on gimbals to minimise needle jumping. George Formby's "Chinese Laundry Blues" blared out across the plains.

They went via I Thought I Told You Not To Be So Ridiculous Valley, and up through the old orchard on the hilly bit of Don't Be So Ridiculous Valley (which was really a hill, so went upwards, don't forget). They were just turning out of the orchard when something heavy bounced off Froon's helmet.

"What was that?" yelled Sodge.

"I think it was haddock and chips twice. It must be Friday" said Ergo.

They followed the stream down the other side of the hilly bit of Don't Be So Ridiculous Valley, until they were able to cross the Unbelievably Smelly River dam, under cover of darkness. Two days later they found themselves at the foothills of the Mauve and Avocado Mountains, and moving towards the Avocado Basin. They were soon to enter pigfrog country! Ergo gave orders for the gramophone to be silenced, and the records to be stowed in the furry envelopes which protected them from breakage and frost damage. They trudged on until teatime on the third day, stopping to make camp and rest. Unknown animals barked eerie warnings across the bleak landscape. Darkness fell. Darkness was one of the clumsiest slugs Ergo had ever met. How can you fall over when you are already lying down? It could be done. Darkness could do it.

Two gnome-adds had come along as cooks, stretcher-bearers, buglers and money lenders. In their capacity as cooks, they now opened several tins of "BEEF, CORNED. Slugs for the use of" and created a magnificent banquet with the help of a tin of "MILK, EVAPORATED" and a large lump of "CHEESE, PROCESSED".

Everyone ate, sang songs and drank Dandelion and Burdock. Yes, this was life, thought Ergo. This was flipping life! He pressed his "Bivouac" button and an ingenious tent contraption sprang out from the base of his slug tray and made itself into a sort of tent roof, rather like the hood of a Mercedes

SL. Ergo slept.

He dreamed that he was playing the piano. We all dream about the unattainable. To a human, dreams of flying are the ultimate fantasy. Ergo dreamed about playing the piano, with real, clever little fingers instead of the knobby little digits he could usually form from his slimy bits. He was singing, too. It was a song he had composed, in his dream. The song was called "Thinking Of Little Else". So! He had not forgotten Elsie at all! There she was, right in the middle of his dream. Poor Elsie, who had lost her brother to a pigfrog. Ergo would avenge her. And he was playing the piano for her... It felt so thrilling to be in love! He started to tingle all through. Far out! If he had had loins they would certainly be stirring now, and no mistake. He thought of Little Else in her tweed jacket. He thought of her in tennis shorts. He thought of her in a grand hotel, eating a French bean salad. He thought of himself sitting next to Little Else, watching her eat the salad. He began to weep warm, salty, loving tears. In his dream, he fell asleep. In reality, he woke up.

There was something watching him from a distance of about fifteen yards. Something not very nice. He could see it through the open doorway of his roof-tent, and at first he thought that he was still dreaming. Looking out across the campsite, he could see the misty, dawn-lit shapes of the rest of his task force, asleep in their individual bivouacs. The intruder was now moving slowly towards him. It was a heavy-set, hairy, humanoid creature, something like a troll. It had very nasty eyes. They were bloodshot, with huge black pupils that bored into Ergo with deadly, detached menace. Its arms, which were long enough to drag along the ground, held a powerful wooden crossbow with a vicious-looking dart or bolt sticking out of it. As it moved, its gait was characterised by the stooping lurch of a hunchback.

Ergo silently started the power system of his wheels. The woodland creature at the back of his machine woke with a start and literally spat onion breath into the windsock. With a swift movement, Ergo rammed the machine into reverse and shot backwards about six feet (all measurements are given in converted slug feet; in reality slugs didn't call them "feet" for obvious reasons). The intruder stopped in its tracks, taken aback by the sudden movement. Ergo rang a loud bicycle bell which was attached to his "handlebars". It woke the camp. Bivouac roofs concertina'd back into their slug tray bases, and the task force was revealed, half asleep. Five other nasty troll things stood around, crossbows ready.

"Don't you lot dare move, or I'll be very cross indeed!" shouted the first troll thing, in rather a posh accent. He appeared to have echo on his voice. It made the voice sound like a cross between Elvis Presley and Prince Charles. It was clear that the task force was surrounded, and that, having been taken by surprise, were powerless against these strong, heavily armed enemies.

"Who are you?" asked Ergo. The chief troll chappie thought Ergo had said "How are you?" with a Scottish accent, and it did not reply. The troll seemed to have been to private school, but looked absolutely horrid (the two things not being mutually exclusive, anyway).

"Would you mind telling me what you think you're doing in The Avocado Bit Of The Mauve And Avocado Mountains?" said the leader.

"We are just on an expedition to find out about the pigfrogs," said Ergo. "Not that it's any of your business," he added, bravely.

"Gosh, how exciting!" said the leader. "Any danger of us lot coming, too?"

Ergo breathed a sigh of relief.

"Yes, if you put that thing down before it goes off and kebabs someone," said Ergo.

The intruders were Avocado Pear farmers who lived underground, in the caves and potholes of the Avocado bit of the Mauve and Avocado Mountains. They had seen the task force arrive, presumed they were avocado rustlers, and crept up on them as they slept.

"I do have a little bit of bad news for you," said the chief avocado farmer.

"What's that, then?" asked Ergo.

"Well, you know how the pigfrogs only come out in December?"

"Yes, of course," said Ergo.

"It's June," said the farmer.

"Oh, dear," said Ergo. "Turn around, lads."

⟞⟝

Down the mountains they trudged. The Avocado farmers helped them to find the way, because they had only brought with them a one-way map. The chief avocado farmer was called Arthur Monkberry, and he had told

26

Ergo that he and his friends would join the great army on its return through The Avocado Bit Of The Mauve And Avocado Mountains. When he had escorted them as far as the Unbelievably Smelly River dam, he waved goodbye (he waved like the Queen) and shouted "Death To All Pigfrogs!" which went down really well.

On the way, Ergo's

thoughts drifted back to Little Else. He was hooked. Couldn't wait to get back home to the Farnsbarnes' Tree House. Formby's "Chinese Laundry Blues" didn't quite seem the same any more. His heart was beating to a different rhythm. The sudden end to his adventure was insignificant by comparison.

As they pulled in to the Farnsbarnes' front garden, Ergo leaped from his wheels in order to run upstairs even before the wheels had come to a standstill. This did not have the effect he had hoped for, which was to get him to Little Else quicker. Having abandoned his wheels he was now only able to move more slowly.

Ah, thought Ergo. He remounted his wheels and waited for the Farnsbarneses and Else to come out to greet them.

Not wishing to appear foolish, the little slug general regained his composure and began a stirring speech to all present. Dismissing the aborted recce expedition as unimportant and a great victory both at the same time, he suddenly hit on a wonderful idea which he deftly ad-libbed into his speech.

"I have a plan," he said. "It is all to do with December – so I bet you I wouldn't have thought of it without the recce, and meeting Arthur Monkberry. Since pigfrogs only come out in December to spoil Christmas, we'll go up there next week and fool them into thinking it is Christmas already! We'll do carol singing, and shake sleigh bells. We'll be nicer to each other than usual, and make a big show of giving each other useless presents which we can't afford and nobody wants! We'll be so overtly festive that they'll come leaping from their potholes, all disorientated, and half asleep, which is when we'll hit them with everything we've got, or preferably more! Ha ha!"

Everybody had to admit it was, well, an interesting idea.

Little Else smiled. She thought it was a brilliant idea. She had had a strange dream the night before, where Ergo had been playing the piano to her. It had been so romantic, and he'd been wearing a grey silk tuxedo with a yellow handkerchief. Up until then she'd always thought of him as just another slug. Now things had begun to feel different, There was a heroic quality to him that she was beginning to find rather magnetic. Vive La Difference! Of course, la difference between fairies and slugs was no laughing matter. It would all probably end in tears, she told herself. She still thought it was a brilliant idea.

And so the plan was laid. Sodge, who was becoming a most able lieutenant to Ergo, put the entire army over a rigorous assault course, each soldier carrying a 60lb pack containing Christmas puddings, Scalextrix sets and bottles of green ginger wine. Dotty organised a choir, and the worst eight singers were split into two groups of four, and given the imaginative names "Carol Singing Squad Number One" and "Carol Singing Squad Number One". Giving them both the same name was a subtlety thought up by Sodge, to fool the enemy. Quite how it would fool them he never said. It certainly fooled the carol singers, however.

Calendars were purchased and filled in with false appointments all the way through June, July, August, September, October and November. No detail was ignored. Nigel went down to the stores and swapped two dozen cans of Breakfast Woodsmoke for a dozen of Essence of Tangerines and Cigars.

It was decided to change the power system of Nige's Wheels. There was nothing wrong with the power, they explained to Nige, diplomatically. It was the idea of spending another night in a bivouac with one's squirreloid partner breaking wind all night from a day's work eating raw onions that had really been the straw that had broken the camel's back. Nige said he understood. A few days later, he came up with a garlic and baked beans powered version.

"Thank goodness for that," they chorused.

$$\sim\!\!\!\downarrow\!\!\!\sim$$

The problem about being in, near, or from Don't Be So Ridiculous Valley was that you could never say "Don't be so ridiculous!" to anyone even if you really meant it, because they would think you were just casually mentioning the place. They might perhaps think you were asking the way there, and direct you to it, and if you were particularly polite, you might start off towards it, so as to avoid offending them. Consequently, nobody ever said it in normal conversation, and so if anybody actually was being ridiculous, it went completely unchecked.

Three weeks after the return from the incident with the avocado farmers (called in slug mythology "the avocado incident"), Ergo and his entire army were ready to leave on the great push into pigfrog country. This time, they were so well-equipped it wasn't funny. Well, maybe it was a bit funny, but not very. Anyway, there they were, all well-equipped and everything, sat sitting on the grass waiting for orders. Dotty and Mr Farnsbarnes were hovering very professionally in the air above the leading ranks of the slugs and auxiliary forces, made up of trolls, gnomes and assorted fairy and woodland folk, some of the Enid Blyton ilk, but most of the Tolkien variety. In fact, many had been

in *Lord Of The Rings*, which was now finished, and they had relocated to find new work.

Dotty's helicopter was now blue with a dark blue stripe, and Mr F's was pink, meaning that it must have been Monday, Wednesday or Friday Afternoon, or Tuesday, Thursday or Weekend morning. It was, in fact 10.30am on a Saturday morning. The helicopters were cunningly disguised as sledges with reindeer, thanks to an ingenious papier mache mould created by Mr

Farnsbarnes. It made them difficult to pilot, but it was possible to get an adequate view by peering between the reindeer antlers and moving one's head about all the time. Ergo had decided on a particularly novel touch. He looked up the pigfrogs in the phone book (under P) and had found out their number. It was Everywhere Else 1453876. He dialled it. It rang and rang. Eventually, a taped message said:

"Hello, this is pigfrog headquarters. Sorry there is no-one here awake to take your call. Please leave a message and we'll get back to you."

Fairly standard stuff, thought Ergo. He had actually wanted to speak to the senior pigfrog, who he had learned was an old bandit called General Moundrot.

As the tone sounded, Ergo began:

"Hello, everybody. Merry Christmas and welcome to another December 24th. We'll soon be on our way past your caves but please take no notice, and don't whatever you do try to jump on us or it will be most unpleasant. Goodwill to all men, but more particularly slugs and pigfrogs one and all."

The machine clicked off and he replaced the receiver.

"That should help" he said, hopefully.

Moving to the head of his forces, Ergo began to give orders.

"Three hundred mushroom burgers, medium rare, no salt," he shouted down his field telephone. Some hours later it was all delivered by a small fleet of vans from the Woodlands Gourmet Take-Away Joint.

"An army marches on its stomach!" opined Ergo, which in this case was especially true. When they had eaten their meal, the slug forces were ready to move.

He had briefed his senior commanders down to the last detail. The forces moved forward in column-of-twos, and the first formation of slugs-on-wheels was followed by two large snow machines, which were pulled by a team of gerbils. Gerbils would go anywhere, and Ergo had been training them for months. He knew they would not fail him in a tight spot.

After these came the combat troops with their party hats and streamers, under which were secreted the deadly weapons especially developed for this mission. The most sophisticated of these was the pigfrog depth charge – wrongly named because it was fired into the air, nowhere near water. But it could be hidden in the back of the trouser belt and fired as the assaulting pigfrog was in mid-air. A specially sensitive ground-vibration and scream-sensitive aerial dragged along the ground to signify the moment that an attacking pigfrog was airborne. Once the trousers were activated the pigfrog would stand no chance, and would, in theory, explode in mid air, spreading pigfrog bits all over the shop. The only problem was that slugs did not wear trousers. Oops. But it was quite good for gnomes and so on. To make up for the mistake about the trousers, Nige had invented a saliva-sensitive hat which could be worn by slugs, so that when a pigfrog was above them, on the descent, so to speak – and most probably dribbling – the saliva-sensitive hat would notify them immediately, and ring a bell.

"What!" said Ergo. "Ring a bell?! That's no flipping good!"

"Oh yes it is," said Nige. "The pigfrog will think it is teatime and look round. This will affect his aerodynamic velocity and he will crash to the ground, probably not on you."

"Oh, do me a favour," Ergo had said. But it was easy to see that Nige had a point. He had, Ergo admitted, been right before. Ergo eventually persuaded Nigel to get rid of the bell and replace it with a high explosive grenade launcher.

The only person left behind, waving from the gate as they went, was Little Else. She bit her lip as they disappeared over the crest of the rising ground adjacent to Chez Farnsbarnes. She had not told Ergo of her feelings for him. Ergo, also, had been too afraid to say anything to her. Perhaps they would never know about the mutual attraction between them, because of their timidness. Choking back a laugh, she turned and wandered back into the house to start the hoovering. The laugh was because she had just imagined herself at the altar, with Ergo crawling up the aisle in a grey top hat. She would not be able to say "Don't be so ridiculous" to him because he might then begin giving her directions to that well-known valley, right in the middle of their wedding! How silly. Her daydream came to an end with a loud bark from the Large Disused Owl, who was practising impressions of various dogs, to keep burglars away in the absence of the other occupants.

Chapter Four: The Sound Of Music

General Moundrot rolled over in the darkness. An incessant drip of slimy goo was landing on and oozing across his face, causing him to snore more loudly and then drop back into a light sleep every few minutes. There was something irritating him. It wasn't the slime – he liked that. Couldn't sleep without it. No, it was something else. Something wasn't normal.

He opened one eye, and rolled his eyeball around as far as he could so as to see across the dark pothole without having to move his head. A small red light was flashing. It was the phone-answering machine. It had clicked in to intercept a call and was now silently announcing the fact that it was ready to communicate.

Moundrot went back to sleep. He slept for another twelve days – the goo constantly dripping down onto the fat, scaly expanse of his left cheek, across his jowl and lower lip, into his mouth and out again through a gap in his front teeth. It wound its way across his forearm and formed little rivulets as it flowed away across the sloping floor. He had chosen to sleep on the upper part of the sloping floor, so that the goo, on leaving his own area, would then benefit the next sleeping pigfrog, which in this case happened to be his wife, Ursula.

It had always been Ursula, from the very first moment they had met, when he and she had both been young pigpoles. Nobody else but Ursula. They had always been known as Ursula and Jim, until he had started to cut a more authoritative figure, and his fast rise through the ranks of the pigfrog military had made it necessary for others to address him as first Captain, then Major, then Colonel, Brigadier and now General Moundrot.

He was not, by any stretch of the imagination, "nice". He had always said it wasn't his job to be liked – even though he could easily have tried it in his spare time. It hadn't occurred to him. To Ursula he was big, warm, sexy, lovable Jim. She never called him Jim in front of the troops, though.

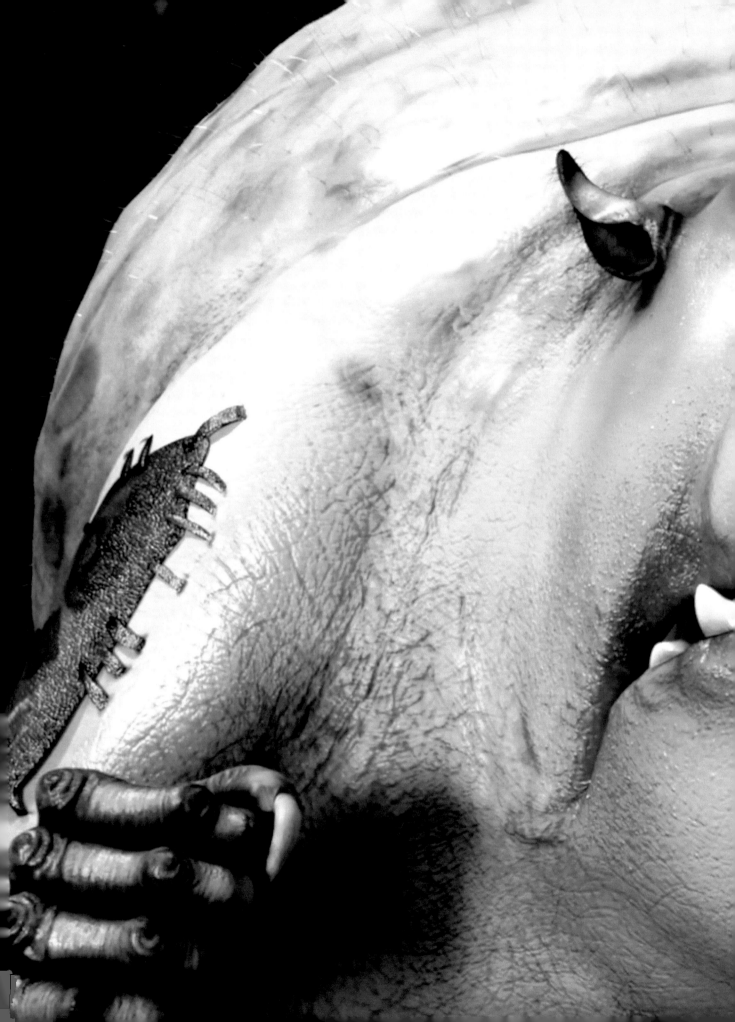

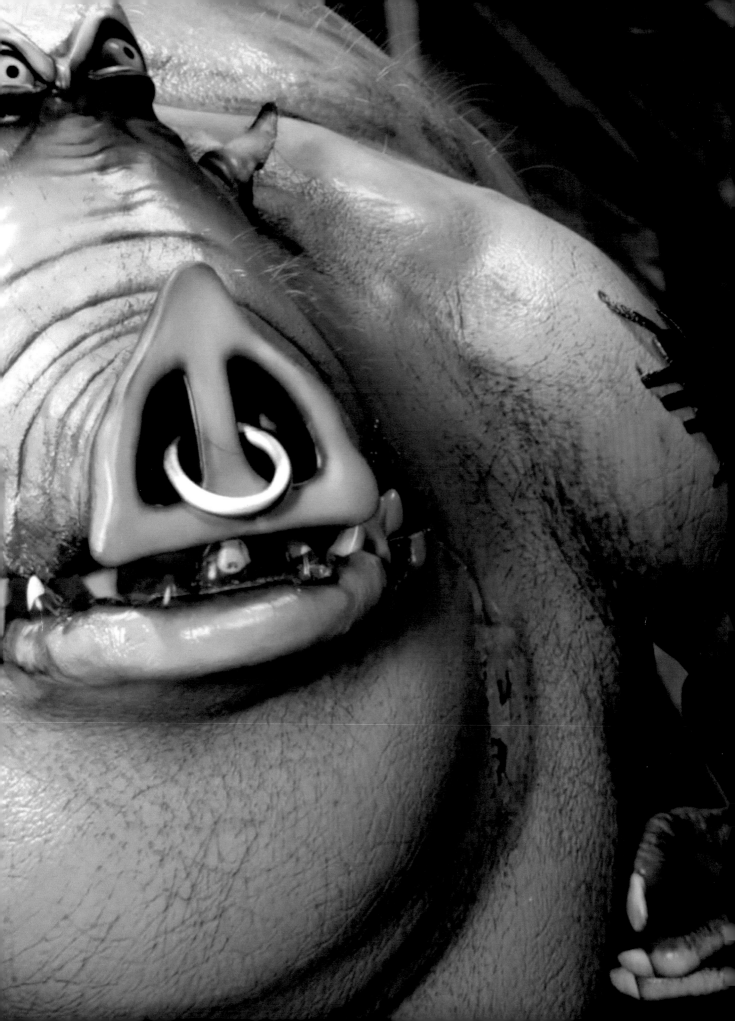

On the thirteenth day, Moundrot's eyes opened. Both together. It was like turning on a light. Switching off a dream. Except he never dreamed. Waste of time. The red light was still flashing. The drip was still dripping, still oozing. He spat. He could hear music. Good, he liked music. Had it been the music that had woken him, he wondered? No, because he'd had a jolly good lie down – about three weeks, as he guessed. It was time to wake up anyway. Ursula was already awake, lying on one side, letting the river of goo ooze reassuringly across the back of her left knee and over her big, muscular thighs.

"Morning, Darling" offered Ursula.

"Achththteupp!" came the sound of Moundrot spitting again, to clear the goo from his jowls and teeth. He always liked to clean his teeth.

"Looks like a lovely day," said Ursula.

How the hell did she work that out, thought Moundrot, knowing that Ursula had no way of knowing whether it was pouring with rain or hailing jelly babies.

"Is it?" he said. He felt tolerant.

"Yes," said Ursula, "and I'm sure we'll have lots of fun."

Moundrot had to admit that the music sounded interesting. There was a knock on the door.

"Who is it?"

"Quirkhardt, Sir."

"Yes, Quirkhardt?"

"There's been a shower of jelly babies overnight, Sir. Can't understand it. Sentries haven't got a clue, either."

Moundrot opened the door.

"Come in, Captain."

The other warrior lurched sheepishly into the room.

"Good Morning, Mrs Moundrot. Good morning, General," began Quirkhardt.

He knew the old boy's moods. Maybe he should not have disturbed him for such a triviality – but it was quite an interesting phenomenon, to say the least.

"We're sweeping them away from the great entrance, Sir, but they appear to be clogging up many of the smaller pothole outlets."

"Don't be so ridiculous!" shouted Moundrot, confident that his inferior officer would not choose that moment to start giving him directions to the well-known valley of that name.

"What sort of jelly babies are they?" he demanded.

"Well, mostly girls, Sir, and all different flavours," stuttered Quirkhardt.

"No, you idiot! I mean are they real ones? Where did they come from? And what's that music, by the way?"

"We're not sure, Sir, but it sounds like carol singers." He knew this would not go down well.

"What? Let me listen. Keep quiet!"

Quirkhardt kept quiet. Moundrot strained himself to listen. There was indeed a distinctly choral sound to it. He could only hear it, very muffled, in the distance, so couldn't be sure.

"It's not Christmas, is it?"

"No, Sir, it's September the twenty-third."

Moundrot felt foolish for mentioning it. This was his September Awakening. There would be food and games, and work, and then more sleep until the

November Awakening, and only then would it be time to get ready for the December Season. Of course it wasn't Christmas.

"Get two sentries out to it immediately!" he barked.

Quirkhardt saluted, turned and leapt down the passageway. He wasn't keen on all this. It wasn't his fault that it had hailed jelly babies, and it wasn't his fault that there were carol singers outside. If there were. He was just doing his job – but he was sure that Moundrot would blame him for it. He did not relish the consequences.

Quirkhardt arrived in the main guardroom, pulling himself together and remembering what it was that made him officer-material.

"Corporal Flighnever, double outside with one inferior of your choice and arrest anybody who might be carol singing," he shouted.

"Yes, Sir." The corporal detailed his chosen helper and made for the main tunnel.

"Oh, and corporal..."

"Yes, Sir?"

"Don't have any fun at all, do you understand?"

"Yes, Sir."

⁓⁄⁓

Squinting through his field glasses, Quirkhardt had a good view of the ground that sloped away from the front entrance of Pigfrog Command. It was uninterrupted for about two hundred yards, and then fell away around the side of a small mountain peak. This obscured his view, but he watched the patrol until they disappeared down into the low area. The sound of the carol singing was fairly constant, coming from that direction. Quirkhardt fancied he also smelled something strange. Cigars – the smell of cigars and, if he wasn't mistaken, tangerines! Yes, it was certainly cigars and tangerines. Christmas smells! It threw him a little. If it hadn't been for the fact that he was Officer Material it might have thrown him a lot, he thought to himself.

Five minutes after the patrol had entered the low ground area Captain Quirkhardt heard a soft, muffled "whump", like a loud, unmuffled "whump" but soft and muffled. A spray of little fragments rose above the ridge and descended like a beautiful firework.

Very pretty, thought Quirkhardt, but if Corporal Flighnever is enjoying himself I'll give him a right good shouting-at.

Quirkhardt need not have worried. Flighnever was not enjoying himself. Indeed, he was at that moment floating off to the pigfrog version of the afterlife, wondering what the hell had hit him. What had hit him was a Slug depth charge, which had been activated by the saliva-sensitive hat of one Fudgebrother the Younger. The corporal, on seeing Carol Singing Squad Number One, had, contrary to orders, crept up behind them and allowed his deadly sense of duty to get the better of him. Instead of arresting them or calling for reinforcements he had unilaterally launched himself, almost instinctively, at the first carol singer in the line – Fudgebrother. As he had come whistling down out of the sky, screaming the pigfrog death-cry, the hat, stimulated by the spray of saliva coming from Flighnever's horrible gob, had triggered the launch of a depth charge and it had all been over in a jiffy. Flighnever, or bits of him, had been the pretty firework which Quirkhardt had seen from Pigfrog Command.

The "one inferior" of Flighnever's choice had escaped and run hell-for-leather back to Pigfrog Command to the strains of "Hark The Herald Angels Sing" and was now skidding up to an alarmed Captain Quirkhardt.

"Captain, they carol singers be nasty little slugs and gnomes and they done in the poor old Corp!" panted the minion.

Meanwhile, several hundred yards from the mouth of Pigfrog Command, an exhilarated slug army was savouring the first blood of the campaign. From his field Headquarters, Ergo was regrouping and positioning his forces for maximum effect in an attack on Pigfrog Command. He was, however, hoping to draw his enemy away from the protection of its underground barracks, and to this end was briefing his senior commanders.

"Phase one of Operation Snowflake has begun, Gentlemen!" he announced. "Under Sodge's command, the special effects unit has started the process of disorientating the enemy and making them question the validity of their own calendars. Some of them must be thinking it is Christmas by now – or at least thinking about Christmas – a dangerous act for a pigfrog, whose instinctive, unconscious reflexes will react to our deception before even the conscious mind is aware of what is going on. This is indicated by the uncontrollable urge which led to the first pigfrog casualty. The sound of carol-singing combined with the natural urge to destroy slugs obviously proved too much for it. We must capitalise on this urge. As we speak, the Farnsbarnes aerial division has completed its jelly baby drop and is creating a snowstorm around the entrances to Pigfrog Command. The Aroma Unit is pumping the cigar and tangerine gas into their ventilation shafts, and our intelligence suggests that they are beginning to be nicer to each other than usual – a sure sign that they think it must be Christmas."

"Phase two will commence as soon as they appear out in the open. We believe they will come out, because they will by now have heard from the escaping patrol member. Their military ethic is such that they will almost certainly send more forces out to deal with the carol singers. At this point CSS No. 1 must retreat far enough for the first pursuing pigfrog patrol to be lured away from and cut off from Pigfrog Command. We would hope that a larger pigfrog army would then be sent after the first. Only then will we attack, as soon as the army reaches the open ground to the front of, but out of sight of Pigfrog Command."

He paused for dramatic effect. So much did he enjoy the dramatic effect that he paused a little longer. Then a little longer. So long did he pause that he forgot what else it was he had been going to say.

"Well, that's about it, gentlemen," he said. "Any questions?"

"Yes, Sir," said Froon, the Library Monitor. "How are you intending to defeat the army once it is in the open?"

"Aha!" said Ergo. "Gather round, Men, here's my plan…"

As they huddled together his voice began to fade away and the lights dimmed to black.

Chapter Five: More Interesting Things Happen

Elsie took the kettle off the stove and poured a large splash of hot water onto her herbal teabag. Must get a new kettle, she thought to herself. The kettle had been taking almost exactly a week to boil lately, which was quite ridiculous, although it was useful as a calendar; but then only if you boiled it constantly over and over again.

It had now been three kettle-boils since Ergo and his lads had marched off into the jaws of Death, or wherever. She hadn't heard back from Ergo at all – but then, as Ergo was not aware that Elsie had begun thinking tenderly of him, there was nothing surprising in that. She had received a postcard from Dotty, saying that all was well as they had passed through The Avocado Bit Of The Mauve And Avocado Mountains, and that Arthur Monkberry had indeed joined the army, with his band of ugly trolls. She had learned of the first Jelly Baby Drop and the depth-charge incident. Elsie put the kettle on again. Through the window of Dotty's kitchen she could see a panoramic view of Don't Be So Ridiculous Valley, the great hill stretching away at the centre. Her mind wandered back to Ergo, and she wished he felt the same stirrings for her as she felt for him. She was certain that he didn't, because he hadn't said anything, and in any case he wouldn't, because, she reasoned, a slug would never even think of any romantic adventure with a fairy. Fairies just weren't attracted to slugs, so why would he even try it? There was no precedent. It wasn't just as if there was a social barrier – in fact there was no social barrier. The problem was purely physical. Slugs were just the wrong shape. No legs, not much in the way of arms. No muscles. Slimy. Come to think of it, she was beginning to have second thoughts now. It was even putting her off her Rosehip and Hibiscus Herbal Infusion. But then, he was sort of cute. And brave, and ambitious, and a leader... would probably become extremely wealthy... yes, he was really rather attractive after all.

She doodled and knitted, whittled a stick, baked a rice pudding, varnished the stairs, phoned her mother, made a model of Don't Be So Ridiculous Valley

Post Office And Town Hall Building out of matches and read the *Woodland Daily Trumpet*, but her mind constantly returned to Ergo. She wondered if she should set out intrepidly to try to find him. Or just set out, unintrepidly. She wandered out onto the balcony and sat down next to the Large Disused Owl. The Owl had no conversation, and smelled rather high, so she returned to the kitchen and walked through to the helicopter loft, which was on the same level. She walked around the remaining helicopter – which must have been Dotty's because it was pink, and it was a Wednesday afternoon. Or was it Nigel's? And was it Tuesday?

An idea began to form in Elsie's head. It was the only place she ever had them.

Yes, it was a good idea! Not quite as good as Ergo's idea about Christmas, but up there with some of the really good ideas you hear about. She began to make her plans, and waited for the kettle to boil once more.

⚜

General James Moundrot was not a happy bunny.

"Quirkhardt!" he barked, "get Third Battalion on Red Alert immediately!"

"Yes, Sir!" returned Quirkhardt. "I think they are already on an alert, but I'm not terribly sure which colour alert they're on."

"Probably Yellow Ochre or Magnolia," snapped Moundrot. He prided himself on a sense of humour in moments of crisis. Quirkhardt laughed, sycophantically.

"Don't stand there laughing sycophantically you dithering clot!" yelled his commander. "Get down to the mess and call all company commanders to the briefing room. Now!"

Once again, Quirkhardt found himself hurtling down the corridors of Pigfrog Command, cursing his luck for having been born. Dithering clot, indeed! Why did the boss keep him on if he was such an idiot? Maybe it was the boss who was a dithering clot... but the thought remained unfinished, because he was now pushing through the swing door of the mess.

"All company commanders of Third Battalion report to the briefing room immediately. Place your soldiers on full Magnolia Alert!" he spluttered. "Red, I mean."

Four minutes later, the six commanders were sitting in the briefing room, waiting for the old man. They didn't have to wait long. Moundrot rolled into the room, dragging his trail of goo, which always seemed to be more or less in one piece and followed him around like a string of elasticated mucous, even though the weight of it compared to its elasticity sometimes meant that it arrived in a room twenty seconds after he did.

"Gentlemen, Christmas appears to have arrived a little earlier this year," Moundrot began, "and it looks as though your appetite for dampening the Christmas Spirits of horrible little slug and woodland civilians will soon be satisfied many times over. However, one of our NCOs has... er... gone to Heaven, as a result of aggressive action from a party of slug carol singers. Even though the deceased was only Corporal Flighnever, so the loss to us is minimal, I intend to locate and eliminate this group of slugs without delay. Third Battalion will carry out this task. Furthermore, you will bring to me all the squashed bits of all enemy casualties, plus at least one live prisoner for interrogation." With that, he lurched out of the briefing room, dragging his goo behind him, and leaving his commanders to formulate their plan.

***

DBSRVAM

It was a cold, freezing morning when Elsie walked down the High Street of Elftown, the only town in Don't Be So Ridiculous Valley. She turned off the main street and into a small alleyway, where there were three tiny shops. The first one was a deserted sandwich bar, the second was a bicycle repair shop, and the third bore the inscription: DBSRVAM. To the uninitiated this was nonsense, or possibly an optician's shop. To those who knew, it was the Don't Be So Ridiculous Valley Academy of Music. She pushed open the shop door and a little bell on a spring tinkled to announce her. It was a single, small shop-room with dusty old bits of sheet music pinned up on yellow wallpaper and an upright piano against one wall. It certainly wasn't a very big Music Academy, thought Elsie. An oldish elf was sitting on the piano stool, reading *The Financial Journal*.

"Good morning," said the elf.

"Good Morning," said Elsie. "I've come to enquire about piano lessons."

"Well, I know it's a bit of a cliche, but you've come to the right place," said the elf. To prove it, he flicked open the lid of the piano and rattled off an

Interior of the Academy of Music

arpeggio of C sharp diminished seventh.

"They're not for me, they're for my… er, a friend of mine," said Else.

"Well, fine," said the elf. "There's no problem. No waiting list, regrettably. In fact she would be my only pupil."

"It's a he," corrected Elsie. "But there is one very tiny problem – he hasn't got any hands. He's a slug, you see," she said, with some embarrassment.

"I see," said the elf, picking up a bright red accordion and starting to play a chromatic scale. "Yes, that does pose a certain… er… challenge."

"But he does have knobbly bits," said Elsie, hopefully. "I do so want to give him a nice surprise as a Christmas present."

"But it isn't Christmas for ages," said the elf.

"I know, but, we… it's very complicated, but Ergo – that's my friend – he is having his Christmas earlier this year… I'll explain it to you later, but in the meantime, what do you think – can you teach him?"

"It might be quite expensive," said the elf, in a worried voice.

"That's fine", said Elsie, taking out a Woodland Shilling and pressing it into his grateful hand. "The only thing is, he is up in the mountains beyond the Avocado Basin, leading an army into battle at the moment, so could you come with me? I have a helicopter which I've borrowed from my sister and I'm not bad at flying it, even though I'm completely self-taught."

The elf thought for a moment, and looked down at the Woodland Shilling. Money talked in Don't Be So Ridiculous Valley.

The money said, "Go on Mate, you'll enjoy yourself."

"OK, then," said the elf. "Shall we take the piano?"

᠊ᢧᢣ᠊

Just as Elsie had been entering the Music Academy on that cold morning, Ergo had been crawling into position with Sodge, on a high vantage point from where he could see, to his left, the entrance to Pigfrog Command. Beyond, and across the sloping ground to his right – out of sight of Pigfrog Command – were the brave members of Carol Singing Squad Number One. Froon was crouching (as much as it makes any difference to a slug) at one corner of the squad, listening intently to his field radio.

"CSS1 in position, Ergo," said Sodge. His cold breath formed into steamy streaks in the air as he talked, an effect enhanced by the layers of artificial snow which now covered the crags and open ground surrounding them. The distant sound of sleigh bells added to the atmosphere of goodwill which prevailed, and nearly made them forget the deadly nature of their mission.

"My Goodness, I nearly forgot the deadly nature of our mission just then," said Ergo.

"Right, Carol Singers – good luck, and off you go," he whispered to Froon over the crackling airwaves.

"Thanks, Boss," returned Froon. The singers struck up "The Holly and the Ivy, When they are both well known, Of all the trees that are in the wood..."

"I've always liked this one," said Ergo fondly, enjoying the stereo effect of the distant, live voices of his friends coming across the cold morning air, combined with the radio version blaring from his headset.

"They do a very fine version of "The Twelve Days Of Christmas" too," offered Sodge, who shared his commander's love of music. Just then, there was a nasty, sickening sucking sound that made Ergo think about the end of the world, and the sound of heavy footfalls coming towards them. Ergo swung round. It was Arthur Monkberry, the chief Avocado troll, coming up to join them on the crag, and sucking a mint humbug.

"Give us one!" said Sodge.

"Sorry, last one," Arthur lied. Throwing down his crossbow, he dropped to his elbows so as to be lying next to Ergo, looking out across the terrain to their front. "Cold day," grumbled Arthur, in his Prince Charles voice.

"Yes," replied Ergo. "Crisp, I think they call it. A good day to eliminate a large number of pigfrogs."

A large number of pigfrogs appeared just as he said the words.

"Wow, did you see that! Just as I said the words "a large number of pigfrogs" about three hundred of them appeared! Synchronicity! Wow!" cried Ergo.

Sodge and Arthur weren't thinking about synchronicity.

"Ergo, there's hundreds of them! You've got to get the singers away, fast!"

Ergo snapped out of his delirium. "Yes. Froon, Froon, Ergo here... start moving down the slope. About three hundred pigfrogs coming towards you. Stay on your guard." Froon was already moving. The carol singing squad had started to move at a gentle pace, a pace which quickened considerably as Ergo spoke the words "three hundred pigfrogs". The slugs in the squad were driving their wheels, and the other beings were running at a good trot. About fifty Woodland metres behind them they could hear the thump and rumble of the approaching pigfrogs.

"Keep singing!" barked Ergo, into Froon's earpiece.

"Silent Night, Holy Night..." began Froon.

"No, no no, something faster!" the others pleaded, and they struck up a bright chorus of "We Wish You A Merry Christmas", which, musically speaking, left much to be desired, on account of their uneven breath control.

"I wish I was back in Don't Be So Ridiculous Valley Municipal Accounts Department," croaked one of the gnome-adds, who had been undecided about whether to come or not, and was now sure.

They ran on, with the pigfrogs bearing down on them. Every time they looked back their pursuers had gained a little more ground.

By now, the leading pigfrogs were beginning to dribble so much at the thought of landing on the group of slug singers that the ones at the back were finding it difficult not to slip over on the saliva of the ones in front; but pigfrogs were built for this kind of thing, and they kept their balance as they crashed onwards, nearer and nearer to Carol Singing Squad Number One.

Then, all at once, the six leading pigfrogs – nasty, heavy duty ones with scowling jowls and quivering claws – launched themselves upwards and forwards, using their powerful legs, and upon reaching their full launch altitude began their descent, screaming like eagles, spitting and dribbling.

At that moment, five of the saliva-sensitive hats and two belt-carried depth charge packs erupted in a salvo, and the six pigfrogs exploded in a spectacular but gut-rending fountain of fire, spit and pigfrog particles.

The carol singers were lying on the ground, exhausted, but Froon was shouting "Get up, men! There are still two hundred and ninety-four of the blighters!" He needn't have worried. The others had turned and were heading back to Pigfrog Command faster than they had made the outward trip.

"Great, Lads! Well done!" shouted Ergo. "Good old Nige! Now keep on moving, Froon, or we won't coax the rest of them out. You have to get out to the flat bit of land so that our army can swoop down on them from the rocks on the other side." Froon's squad gamely picked themselves up and trudged outwards a little further. They reloaded their hats and checked themselves for bruises.

Little Elsie and the elf wheeled the piano down the High Street and over some nasty cobblestones until they came to the recreation ground where Else had parked the helicopter.

"I hope you realise it will need tuning now," said the elf.

"I think it needed tuning before!" replied Elsie, slightly ruffled from the physical effort of moving the piano. She went round to the back of the helicopter and took out a ramp which Ergo often used to crawl into the back seat.

"That'll be good for your slug friend to lie on whilst playing the piano," said the elf. Elsie was beginning to like the elf now. He seemed thoughtful. They pushed the piano up the ramp but they couldn't get it into the helicopter. Not to be beaten, Elsie carefully roped it to the helicopter so that it would hang underneath as they flew. They strapped themselves in and took off with a loud roar.

"Ergo will be so delighted when we arrive with a piano!" exclaimed Elsie, excitedly. "I know he will just love learning to play it!"

They rose up above the rooftops and the trees of the Valley, and could see for miles, out across I Thought I Told You Not To Be So Ridiculous Valley, which was situated to the north, and away even beyond that, to the land known as Everywhere Else.

"I'm sorry the engine is so noisy!" shouted Elsie. "It runs on tea, and I put Camomile tea in, thinking it wouldn't matter, but it obviously doesn't like it very much. Seems to get us from A to B, though."

The trouble was, whereas Elsie knew where "A" was, (where they were now), she didn't know much about where "B" was, (where they were going to). She knew that Ergo was up beyond the Avocado Basin, but had no idea other than that. She did have a map of The Avocado Bit Of The Mauve and Avocado Mountains and so she decided to follow the Unbelievably Smelly River up to its highest point, and then ask someone.

Chapter Six: Don't Squash The Piano Player

Quirkhardt waited at the entrance to Pigfrog Command for the last stragglers of Third Battalion to retreat to its safety. Being Officer Material wasn't helping him much now. He was terrified. Not of the enemy, but of old Moundrot when he found out about the six more warriors who had gone to Heaven. And one of them had been Sergeant-Major Hardsnot, the battalion mud-wrestling champion. Quirkhardt knew that Moundrot's anger might not be satisfied with a verbal outburst – though that would be bad enough. The old boy was apt to lash out when really angry, and this could easily be one of those moments, Quirkhardt thought. He could feel the pain already. It occurred to him that he could run away – but that would be desertion, punishable by death. He could feign illness. No, that would cut no ice with Moundrot. Or... yes, or, ...or! ...he could convert this little setback into a victory before the General ever found out about it. Yes! *Major* Quirkhardt had a nice ring to it! That's what he would do. Yes, yes! Officer material to the rescue! The General didn't yet know – he had not yet received any report of the action. So Quirkhardt would send Third Battalion right back in against those upstart slugs and assorted Woodland beings... right now, before the General could hear about that little incident earlier. But this time they would crush the enemy – literally!

And so this was how it came to be that Third Battalion appeared once again outside the opening of the main entrance of Pigfrog Command. Quirkhardt was sure they could overpower such a small carol singing group, even with it having this secret weapon thing. Goodness gracious, they had never had trouble with carol singers before! He would place the most dispensable, idiotic soldiers, whom he knew Moundrot wouldn't mind losing, at the front, and then, when the secret weapon went off, the other warriors would keep on running forward and launch themselves at the carol singers before they had a chance to reload the weapon things. If he lost another six or eight bodies, but eliminated the enemy, so what! It would still be a victory!

What Quirkhardt did not know was that Carol Singing Squad Number One was not the only slug contingent ranged against him.

By the time the pigfrog battalion had spotted Froon's unit it was out on the open ground, but protected by the unseen presence of the main force, hidden in the rocks not far off. Running forward, the pigfrog army set up a terrifying vibration, but their pace was slightly nervous, remembering the results of their last attack.

Ergo got on the blower to Froon. "Here they come, Froon, but don't worry – we're here. Just you keep singing, Mate."

Froon's unit started up again, "While Shepherds Watched..." and the pigfrog army bore down on them with terrifying speed. This time, the carol singers stood their ground. Quirkhardt, leading from the back of Third Battalion, had fire in his eyes and faith in his heart. "Let's give those yukky little so-and-so's a Merry Christmas!" he shouted as the huge mass of pigfrog flesh moved as one towards its tiny target. The leading pigfrogs leaped – admittedly a little more gingerly in the light of the recent incident – and began their descent. But leaping more gingerly did not prove to offer any safety advantages over leaping less gingerly. Once again, the depth charges found their dribbling targets and the sky was filled with pigfrog remnants and big streaks of spit. But this time, the pigfrogs at the rear came stampeding on. But just as the second wave of pigfrogs was reaching its natural jump-off point, the slug army appeared from the rocks to their left. These were the Elite Force of crack slug troops, on their wheels, handlebars bristling with shiny weapons and banners, balloons, holly and streamers. The shock of this complication caused many of the enemy to skid to a halt, while others fell over them. This gave rise to such disarray that they were unaware of Froon's unit's escape, away to the right and up towards Ergo's vantage point.

Just at that moment Ergo, supported by Arthur's trolls, advanced down from the high ground behind Third Battalion, trapping them in a pincer movement. A volley of troll crossbow darts went singing through the air, and seventeen more members of Third Battalion were dispatched to the Afterlife.

But this is supposed to be a happy story, so I won't go into the details of what happened next to the pigfrogs. Even if they deserved what they got, it's all a bit gruesome for our story, particularly if small children are reading this or being read to. Let's just say that before too long, there were pigfrog pieces all over the place, pigfrogs with their intestines hanging out, lying in

the dust; headless pigfrogs and pigfrogless heads, charred pigfrog carcasses with horribly contorted faces, eyes hanging out and blood everywhere. That sort of thing. In fact, I'm beginning to feel really sorry for the pigfrogs now.

Ergo watched the remnants of Third Battalion retreating back to Pigfrog Command, led, this time from the front, by the hapless Captain Quirkhardt. Ergo felt sorry for them, too. This was only supposed to have been an Adventure. He had forgotten that ridding the world of Evil Pigfrogs would inevitably involve really killing them. You could hardly capture them and make them promise to be good, could you? They weren't Naughty Goblins,

they were nasty, horrible, bloodthirsty, evil, slug-squashing, fairy-crushing, Christmas-hating creatures, and then some.

The day was not without slug casualties, though they were few. As the smoke cleared, they discovered the remains of old Erk, the warrior slug who had seen so much action. He had been squashed by retreating pigfrogs, not even killed in a fair fight. Also, Slarjk, the flower cutter, was suffering from a really nasty headache and dizzy spells.

"C'est la gare," said Ergo, in his Napoleon voice.

"That means 'This is the station'," said Froon, undiplomatically. "Don't you mean, "C'est la guerre" – meaning "That's war?"

"Just because you're the library monitor doesn't mean you have to show off," said Ergo.

Just then a piano dropped out of the sky and hit him on the head.

"Flipping Heck!" shouted Ergo, who would have fallen over but for the fact that he was already lying down. His cap-shaped helmet had protected him from a right good squashing.

"Ergo, Ergo, are you alright?" shouted Little Else as she guided the chopper downwards to a clear space to the side of the troops.

"Elsie, what are you doing here? You should be back at home, varnishing the stairs," said Ergo, rubbing his head and rather wishing the piano had not fallen out of the sky onto it.

"I'm sorry about that, Ergo, it was supposed to be your Christmas surprise," said Elsie. "But are you OK?"

"Well, it certainly was a surprise – but don't worry, it's only a flesh wound," said Ergo. "Good job it landed on my head."

"I thought slugs only had flesh," said Elsie.

"Well, if brains and kidneys and things like that are counted as flesh, I suppose you're right," said Ergo.

"Gosh, I didn't know slugs had kidneys," said the piano-playing elf, fascinated.

Ergo looked round at the elf. "Who's this, Elsie?" he asked.

"His name – well, I don't actually know his name, but he's my Christmas present to you, Ergo!" announced Else.

"Well, thanks, Else. A slave, you mean?"

"No, no, silly boy. A piano teacher!"

The elf did a little twirl and took off his cap. A tear appeared in Ergo's eye. The idea of piano lessons was wonderful enough, but the fact that they were a gift from the most beautiful, tweed jacket-wearing, cute-voiced fairy he knew – about whom he dreamed at night – was almost too much. In fact, it was too much. Ergo fainted.

"Oh, great!" said Froon. "Now our supreme commander is unconscious and we're still in the heart of pigfrog territory. That's great, that is!"

"And I bet they're cross," chipped in Slarjk, whose headache had improved, if only by comparison to Ergo's. (Erk was still dead, however.)

"Oh, I'm sorry," said Elsie. "Let's get Ergo into the helicopter and then you others can take cover."

A troll and two squirreloid things lifted Ergo into the helicopter and Elsie and the piano-elf got into the front seat. They had agreed to meet everyone at a mountain peak just a few hundred Woodland metres away, to regroup. The army marched off as soon as the helicopter was airborne. After a minute or two of flying, Else realised she'd forgotten to load the piano back onto the helicopter. All that effort, and the piano was left behind in pigfrog country! She'd just have to go back. She did a cute little turn in the air and landed again beside the piano. Ergo was, by now, waking up and wondering where he was. He thought he was back in Don't Be So Ridiculous Valley eating fish and chips in the orchard on a Friday night.

"Pass the vinegar," he moaned. When no-one did, he snapped out of his dream and took command of the situation.

"Quickly, Else! Get that piano on board! – I'd help but I don't have any arms!" said Ergo.

Elsie and the elf tried hard, but it was taking rather a long time. They struggled with the ramp. Eventually, they had the piano balanced on the sill of the helicopter door opening, half in and half out. Ergo was actually helping by pushing and pulling with his wheels, even though he had now resorted to geared stomach muscle power on account of the fact that his woodland creature had been separated from him during the battle. Stopping for a brief rest, Elsie said, "What's that music?" They all listened. Sure enough, there was a distant sound of cellos and kettle drums, getting louder. It had begun just as they had started to feel that it was time they were up and away with the piano, in case the pigfrogs arrived. It was adding to their feeling of urgency, and mounting all the time, with their growing concern to get away quickly. Then some tremolo violins came in, which added to the tension. Ergo, Else and the elf worked harder and harder to get the piano into the helicopter. By now, they were getting very worried that the pigfrogs might arrive at any moment. The music got even more exciting. It was film music!

"It's film music!" said Ergo.

"But this isn't a film, it's a book!" said Elsie, incredulously.

"Well, let's not stay to find out; I'm sure the pigfrogs will be here any minute, judging from that music."

"That's where you are wrong...we're here already," said General Moundrot.

Everything went dark.

Chapter Seven: Some More Things Happen

Dotty and Nige were worried. They had not been present at the battle, preferring to fly briefly back home after the jelly baby drop and feed the cat, Euphoria. They knew that Elsie would have been feeding Euphoria, but they still felt that they should pop back to make sure everything was alright. Another important reason why they needed to visit their home was that Nigel's underwater onion peeler was being advertised in the *Woodland Daily Trumpet* and they wanted to buy a copy so that they could see their advertisement.

"Onions without tears, the best thing in years!" read the heavy type at the top of the advertisement. Nigel was not only a genius, but more than that – a talented advertising copywriter as well. At least, Nigel thought so. They bought sixteen copies to send to their friends. They left the offices of the *Woodland Daily Trumpet* and flew straight to the tree house. The Large Disused Owl was pleased to see them, but said nothing. They just knew he was.

Euphoria was ecstatic to see them, because since the departure of Little Else, she had not been fed – a matter of three days.

The reason Dotty and Nigel were worried was of course that Elsie was gone, and had taken Nigel's helicopter. They had no idea why she would have just left like that – they did not know that she had taught herself to pilot it, or that she had quite happily flown off with the piano elf on a perfectly pleasant mission. More ominously, they did not know that she had been ambushed by pigfrogs, along with Ergo, and was probably dead, or at least feeling sick.

They rang everybody they could think of, but no luck. This didn't take long because they couldn't think of many people to ring. The kettle, having been put on by Elsie before she left, was about half boiled, so they knew she had been gone about half a week (unless she had popped back after a day or two to put the kettle on, or put it on a long time before she left). Dotty, being Elsie's sister, was just a bit more worried than Nigel. But then it was Nigel's helicopter, so perhaps they were both worried by about the same amount.

Possibly Dotty slightly, slightly more. There wasn't a lot in it, to be honest.

"I know! We'll call Ergo on his field telephone. He'll know what to do! Hip, Hip, Hooray!" shouted Dotty.

So they did. But it rang and rang, and nobody answered.

"Strange," said Dotty. "He must be away from it. I'll try it later."

Nigel burst into tears.

"Mr Farnsbarnes! Do grow up!" said Dotty. But she knew how he felt.

☀

Ergo had three headaches. One from the piano falling on his head, one from fainting, and one from being "arrested" by the pigfrogs – which had probably involved a short, sharp blow to the anterior cranium. Well, at least he wasn't, you know, dead.

He looked around him as he awoke for the second time that day, in a groggy condition. There was one window – quite big, actually, for a prison. He presumed he was in a prison. The window was more French window sized, with bars, and you could look out across a kind of courtyard area which dropped away from the window and also rose high above the window. His impression was that he was in one of several cells which looked out onto this dark pit of a courtyard. Dark, that was, except for a clean shaft of light which cut the darkness from very high above, where he presumed the deep pothole shaft gave way to fresh air.

But what of Little Elsie? And the piano elf? Had they survived the ambush? What if they hadn't? What if the pigfrogs had just squashed them, but kept Ergo for questioning or ransom or something? All the possibilities went through his mind in a split second – and none of them were pleasant. Ergo was thoroughly miserable. He wished he had never left home, never met the Farnsbarneses, never met Elsie... hey, steady on! That wasn't true! He could never wish that. But he was, shall we say, not feeling Christmassy any more.

"Food for the prisoner in the condemned cell," came the muffled shout from one guard to another. There was a bang outside, and a jangle of keys. Ergo tensed up as a huge pigfrog jailer came lurching into the cell.

"'Ere you are, you slimy little weed," said the jailer, throwing down some disgusting looking muck on a square metal plate that looked like a TV dinner – but not of course to Ergo, as they did not have television in Don't Be So Ridiculous Valley.

"Condemned cell!" said Ergo. "Is it really the condemned cell?"

"Certainly is, me little sluggy effort thingy!" said the jailer. "Plumbing's atrocious, there's damp half way up the walls, the stonework's all cracked. It's going to have to come down."

"Ah," said Ergo, somewhat relieved.

The jailer left the cell after giving Ergo a playful kick in the ribs, which didn't hurt because Ergo didn't have any. The food smelled so bad that Ergo thought he could feel a fourth headache coming on, until he realised to his relief that it was only the third one getting worse.

What could he do? He would obviously try to escape, but how? And could he try to find out whether Else and the piano chappie were still alive? As he ruminated (which he hadn't done for quite a while) he heard a distant tinkling. A piano! Far away above, muffled and distant. It was pretty bad playing, he thought. Maybe the piano elf was teaching Elsie in another cell. Maybe everything was alright – well, as alright as possible in the circumstances. He lay back and allowed himself some moments to listen to Elsie as he imagined, playing through her piano lesson.

$$\sim\!\!\iota\!\!\iota\!\!\sim$$

"Plink... plonkaplong... plinkety plong plong plong," went Ursula Moundrot's horrid fat pigfrog fingers, for it was she. She stabbed and jabbed without much finesse, as she herself would have been the first to admit, or with no finesse at all, as her husband would have said, had she asked him, which she hadn't.

"I thought you told me you could play one of those things," he moaned. "I wouldn't have got Quirkhardt to carry it up all those stairs if I'd known what a useless player you were. Well, yes, I would – but I'd have got him to carry it back down again straight away, which I'll do tomorrow anyway. Up and down the twenty four flights of stairs for eight days, just to start his punishment, and demoting him by one rank a day so that he gradually reaches the rank of lance corporal on the day he dies of exhaustion." The punishment had a nice, creative, satisfying sting to it. Gradual demotion, and then death. Haha! General Moundrot allowed the edges of his slobbering mouth to rise into the faintest hint of a smile.

"It does need tuning," said Ursula, oblivious to the fate of poor Captain – (or was it Lieutenant now?) – Quirkhardt. "I'll get the workshops to give it a tweak this evening."

"Yes that'll make heaps of difference," said Moundrot, sarcastically.

"What about that slug thing you captured, Darling?" asked Ursula, idly.

"We need to find out some things from it. It'll squeal like a... well, it'll squeal," said Moundrot. "We have ways of making them squeal."

"I didn't know slugs could squeal," said Ursula, beginning a rather unsure harmonic minor scale on the piano.

"Oh yes, they can – and this one will!" said Moundrot. "We'll just get you to play the piano to it! That'll do the trick – it'll soon be begging us to stop!"

Ursula didn't get the joke. She pursed her lips and frowned in annoyance, but she didn't descend to his level. She was above all that.

There was a knock on the door.

"Enter!" The door opened and in fell Major Accuppa, the head of catering. He clicked his heels and saluted.

"Sir! The snack you ordered." Two pigfrog waiters trudged in with a trolley, upon which was an array of fine cheeses and fruits, several bottles of highly expensive brandy and a large chocolate cigar. Moundrot hated smoke and cigars but loved the idea

66

of having one in his mouth, so he often had a chocolate one delivered with his evening snack. It had been the cigar smell coming down the ventilation shaft which had most annoyed him about the recent slug attack, not so much the decimation of Third Battalion, although that was pretty annoying. It might even have been a long-held hatred of cigar smoke which had subconsciously driven him to excel at Christmas-spoiling as a young officer rising through the ranks of the pigfrog army.

Major Accuppa saluted and followed his two underlings out of the room. Ursula continued plinking. Moundrot looked up at the wet ceiling with its goo dripping comfortingly down the wall. Life wasn't so bad. He thought happily about the fun he was going to have being extraordinarily unpleasant to the slug prisoner in the morning. He began to feel almost generous. He might even make the nasty little elf prisoner give Ursula some more lessons on the piano. It was Christmas, after all.

⁓⦙⁓

Elsie flew faster and faster, onwards and onwards until she came to the familiar town and the lovely, rolling hill that was Don't Be So Ridiculous Valley. She followed the Woodland Railway until it came out of the hill part of the Valley to the valley part of I Thought I Told You Not To Be So Ridiculous Valley, (which really was a valley, so that's alright) – where she spotted the tree house from her position up in the clouds as she flew along. As she flew down, she thought about the lucky escape she had had, and worried about Ergo and the elf – but mainly about Ergo.

She wondered at how lucky she had been – instinctively when danger threatened – to have remembered that she was a fairy, and that she could fly! All by herself without any silly helicopter! Pah! Easy! And how she had ripped off her tweed jacket, revealing her wings, and how, still carrying the jacket, she had jumped into the air just as Moundrot had swung out at her, so that his fist had landed squarely on the jaw of his nearest junior non-commissioned officer, knocking him to the ground. She remembered with horror how she had seen them dragging Ergo and the elf away, and she wondered whether she would ever see them again. She had reasoned that it was better for her to escape to raise the alarm than to share the fate of her friends, even though she had felt guilty leaving them. She had flown back to the troop lines of the regrouped slug army, and had broken the terrible news to them.

"Gosh, how utterly, utterly crummy!" Arthur Monkberry had said.

"Let's set up camp," Sodge had suggested. "At least we can cook some CHEESE, PROCESSED, Slugs-For-The-Use-Of, and some more of that MILK, EVAPORATED, to cheer us up." So they pitched their tents and sprung open the hoods of their wheelieboards and settled sadly down for the night. Sodge had stayed up late and tried hard to think about what they might do to rescue their leader. Life without Ergo would be terribly... erm, different.

In the morning, Sodge, Arthur and Elsie agreed that Elsie would fly back to the Tree House. Knowing that Dotty and Nige were there, they had decided to ask them to help again, using the remaining helicopter (Nigel's had been captured in the pigfrog ambush). It had been decided that any rescue attempt would best be coordinated by Sodge, from the front line, but using the additional airborne capabilities of Dotty, Nige and Little Else – albeit with only one helicopter.

—͙

As she alighted on the balcony, Else called out, "Cooeee, Dot, Cooeee, Nige!", but there was no reply. She walked into the main room, but it was empty. She walked a little further, but the place seemed deserted. She ventured a little further, into the bedroom, and there they were, sitting up in bed, putting the underwater onion peeler through a sea trial with a bowl of water resting on their knees. They had been so absorbed that they hadn't seen her come in.

"Little Else!" shouted Dot, jumping out of bed and running over to Elsie, spilling the water all over Nigel's lap.

"Aaagh! Blither!" shouted Nigel, temporarily infuriated.

"Elsie, Darling, what happened to you?" said Dotty.

"And where's my helicopter?" added Nigel.

"Mr Farnsbarnes! Elsie is more important than your helicopter! Don't worry, Elsie, you just relax and tell us where the Hell you have been!" said Dotty, kindly.

"Well, I was with this elf, and we had this piano..." began Else.

"Yes, go on..."

"You see, I had wanted to give Ergo a nice Christmas present of some

piano lessons, and so I went to see an elf at the Don't Be So Ridiculous Valley Academy of Music, and we went with the helicopter up to pigfrog country and poor old Ergo got sort of accidentally hit on the head by the piano and then captured, and so did the elf, but the elf didn't get hit on the head by the piano, only Ergo did, and I managed to escape by remembering that I am a fairy and that I can fly without any silly helicopter... well, nice helicopter. And that's about it, here I am! And poor old Ergo's captured and it's all my fault."

Dotty looked at Nige and Nige looked at Dotty. They did believe it of course, because it was less silly than everything else that had happened, but they were terribly upset to think of Ergo, either squashed or lying in some dark and miserable pothole of a pigfrog jail.

The phone rang. It was Sodge and Arthur.

"We're going to storm the place!" said Sodge.

"Ooh, that doesn't sound too bright," said Dotty. "You'll all be squashed".

"Well, have you got a better idea?" asked Sodge, huffilly.

"Nope," admitted Dotty, and the others agreed.

"Do you know that Ergo is definitely in there, and alive?" asked Nigel.

"Yes," said Sodge. "Last night one of our patrols was creeping past pigfrog command and heard a piano playing..."

"That doesn't prove anything," interrupted Elsie.

"No, wait a minute," continued Sodge. "The playing was very simple and clear, and was coming from a window slit, high up in the rock face of the North wall of Pigfrog Command. At first our patrol thought it was just somebody learning to play – badly – until one of them noticed it was playing morse code! And the morse code said "E. R.G.O. A.N.D. E.L.F. A.R.E. A.L.I.V.E. A.N.D. H.A.V.I.N.G. A. H.O.R.R.I.D. T.I.M.E. B.U.T. W.E. E.X.P.E.C.T. A. R.I.G.H.T. G.O.O.D. S.Q.U.A.S.H.I.N.G. A.N.Y. M.O.M.E.N.T. N.O.W. P.L.E.A.S.E. H.E.L.P. ...E.R.G.O. I.S. I.N. J.A.I.L. B.L.O.C.K. F.O.U.R. A.N.D. I. A.M. I.N. M.O.U.N.D.R.O.T.S. R.O.O.M.S. T.E.A.C.H.I.N.G. T.H.I.S. F.A.T. O.L.D. P.I.G.F.R.O.G. T.O. P.L.A.Y. B.U.T. U.S.U.A.L.L.Y. I. A.M. I.N. C.E.L.L. B.L.O.C.K. F.I.V.E....L.O.V.E. F.R.O.M. T.H.E. E.L.F. B.Y.T.H.E.W.A.Y. M.Y. N.A.M.E. I.S. H.O.R.A.C.E.""

Good old Horace the Elf had thought up a ripping wheeze – to use Ursula's piano lessons as a signal, and had written a special tune with a morse code message in it, all on one note. He had taught it to Ursula so that she would play it even if he wasn't there any more. And, boy, did she play it! Over and over again, she was playing it, and the passing slug patrol had heard it!

"Hip, Hip, Hooray!" shouted Elsie, and the others agreed. Ergo was alive!

Then Else stopped and looked up at the ceiling, as if having another fantastic idea. Yes, here comes another one, she thought.

"I've got a better plan than storming the place!" she cried. "I'll dress up as a washerwoman and knock on their door and when they let me in, I'll find my way to Ergo's cell and give him my clothes and he can get out dressed up as me dressed up as the washerwoman. And then I'll put on some other clothes I'll have taken in, and make my escape dressed up as another washerwoman!"

There was a short pause as the others considered the idea.

The short pause was followed by a long pause.

"Why don't you just give Ergo the clothes you take in, and you stay in the ones you are wearing?" said Nigel.

"Oh, yes," said Elsie, "silly me."

"But why should they let a washerwoman in?" asked Sodge, still a distant voice on the field radio.

"Washerwomen always get into places," said Elsie, knowingly. "I think it's a very good plan, even though I do say so myself."

They all agreed that Elsie was a very brave fairy even to think of the idea, let alone be willing to do it. Sodge agreed to wait three days before launching his offensive on the rock face of Pigfrog Command, to give Elsie a chance to carry out her plan.

Chapter Eight: A Very Exciting Bit

Every day that Ursula's passion for the piano lasted was another day when Second Lieutenant Quirkhardt wouldn't have to carry it up and down the stairs of the pigfrog headquarters. If the General's wife was playing it, it was hardly likely to be available for being carted up and down the stairs. Or so Quirkhardt reasoned. He sat in his cell, looking out across the dark courtyard, his feet in irons and his career in ruins – in fact, his career was in fast rewind. Tomorrow, he would be a Regimental Sergeant Major, and the next day, a Company Sergeant Major. The ignominy of it!

By now, Moundrot had softened towards him. He was not going to work Quirkhardt to death – just until he was critically ill. This was fabulous news! To Moundrot, who considered rank to be of paramount importance, Quirkhardt's gradual demotion was the really juicy bit of the punishment. The physical stuff was just a bit of a laugh. However, Quirkhardt was still terrified by the prospect, and was wishing he could somehow escape his shackles and run for it – but he was beginning to feel that perhaps he just wasn't clever enough.

Each morning he heard the next cell being unlocked, and a guard ordering out the elf in the cell next to his, and pigfrogmarching it away to give Ursula her piano lesson. On the third morning, just as he went from Second Lieutenant to Regimental Sergeant Major, Quirkhardt was shocked when the door was pushed open and a dishevelled-looking slug was thrown into the cell, landing beside him with a sluggy, splatty thud.

"Excuse me," said Ergo (for it was he), "but they've demolished my cell – it was condemned, you see – and apparently there wasn't anywhere else to put me." He was a bit daunted by Quirkhardt, who was five times Ergo's size, but at least he was in leg irons, which ruled out any form of physical attack.

Quirkhardt was horrified and insulted by sharing a cell with a nasty little slug, but didn't have the energy to complain. Apart from that, he was too busy

trying to think of a way of escaping.

Ergo was past caring. He was a bit surprised to see a pigfrog Warrant Officer in leg irons, in a cell, but that was the extent of his reaction.

"What are you in for?" asked Ergo, sociably.

"I'm not telling you, you horrible little slippery git," said Sergeant Major Quirkhardt.

"Suit yourself," said Ergo, moving over to the window grill to have a look out into the dark shaft beyond, as if it were a beautiful view of countryside. "I'm a prisoner of war, myself."

Quirkhardt shot Ergo a dark look. This was one of the slug staff officers whom he'd been fighting only three days earlier! Outrageous! Here in the same cell! And now, by dint of his own demotion, the horrible thing was the senior officer in the cell! Uuuurgh. Quirkhardt shuddered. Life had a way of dumping on you just after it had dumped on you, and just before it dumped on you again, he thought.

Ergo was thinking about escaping. Quirkhardt was thinking about escaping. But neither knew that the other was thinking about escaping. It was a bit like Ergo and Little Else being in love with one another and not telling each other, but completely different.

Ergo began to hum a tune. It was a George Formby tune called "The Blue Eyed Blonde Next Door" but only the tune, not the words.

Quirkhardt snapped, "Do you have to hum that?"

"What would you prefer me to hum?" retorted Ergo.

"Well, nothing, can't you just hum to yourself, silently?" asked Quirkhardt.

"It helps me to think about my escape plan," said Ergo.

"Escape plan!" shouted Quirkhardt. Then, thinking that the guards might overhear, he repeated it in a whisper, "Escape plan? What escape plan?" He couldn't believe he was talking to a slug like this. In fact he had never spoken to a slug before at all, even though he had squashed quite a few in his time.

"Well, I'm just wondering what happened to the helicopter," said Ergo, who was really trying to find out whether this pigfrog knew anything.

"What, the pinky-blue one that keeps changing colour?" said Quirkhardt.

"That's the one!"said Ergo. "Where is it?"

"Down at the bottom of the shaft," said Quirkhardt. "The General ordered it to be put there so that the slug... er... army would never have use of it again. He wants to try to get it going. Pigfrog mechanics are even now trying to work out how to fly it, as we speak, at this very moment and at a time not very much, if at all, which I doubt, removed from the present."

"We must try to get to it," said Ergo, who was convinced he would be able to pilot it with a bit of luck and a following wind.

"I know the way to the helicopter, down... er, lots of stairs," said Quirkhardt, "but even if we could get out of the cell, how do we get through the corridors without being detected? I'm very well known here, and you are, erm, a slug, if you don't mind my saying so."

"Not at all, in fact I'm proud of it," said Ergo. "I'm a General, you know."

Quirkhardt couldn't bear it. What had he done to deserve this? Well, of course, he knew what he'd done – he'd led Third Battalion to its doom, but that was all – it wasn't as if he'd been rude to Moundrot or anything. He looked down at the slug to whom he was supposed to look up. He was damned if he was going to look up to it.

"We could dress up as washerwomen!" said Ergo.

"Why washerwomen?" asked Quirkhardt, as if Ergo had taken leave of his senses.

"They are hardly likely to stop two washerwomen, are they?" said Ergo, jubilantly.

"Won't they think it's a little strange, two washerwomen just wandering about?" asked Quirkhardt.

"Yes, they'll probably think, "Strange, two washerwomen wandering about," but they won't necessarily stop us. I mean, would you stop two washerwomen?" asked Ergo, not really needing an answer.

"OK, but where do we get the washerwomen outfits from?" asked Quirkhardt.

"Well, we could adapt our own clothes a little; I've got my hat, pocket handkerchief and armour, and you've got your uniform. We only need skirts – let me see... we could use the napkins from the room service trays! Ha ha!"

Quirkhardt had never thought of it as room service. He'd thought of it as pigswill – but then he liked pigswill, so that was alright. The idea had some merit. Not very much, but some. Anyway, what did he know, he was only a Sergeant Major, and in three days' time he would be a Corporal – and this character was a General. He shrugged.

"Flipping Heck!" said Ergo. "This might work! Let's get going."

So it was that this odd couple, these two natural born enemies, began striving together to create their disguises, plotting and planning their escape from the dark and dreary dungeons of Pigfrog Command. Ergo was still thinking about Little Else. Had it been her playing the piano, or was she dead? It would be bad enough if she just had a sprained ankle, but death was so much more permanent, somehow.

⸎

Little Else was excited and scared. In her bag, she had all her equipment – a radio whistle to summon help, a special sleep-dagger that Nigel had invented, which knocked the enemy out when you stuck it into them, instead of killing them (because Elsie couldn't stand the sight of blood), a flask of tea and a cheese sandwich with mayonnaise and a little pepper.

She loaded her bag into the helicopter, which was pink, because it was Dotty's, and it was a Friday morning. Nigel and Dot got into the two front seats and the helicopter lurched skywards with a great roar. Nigel had filled the tank with the right kind of tea, and everyone felt that the mission had really begun.

"Sodge here, come in, Dot," crackled Sodge's voice over the radio.

"Dot to Sodge, Dot to Sodge, receiving with a rare and extraordinary clarity," replied Dotty, keenly.

"Right, good morning everybody," said Sodge. "I'll keep radio contact until you get up beyond the Avocado Basin and then I'll go off the air in case the enemy are listening."

Pigfrogs didn't have radios, but Sodge wanted to do things correctly. What if they had learned how to use Nigel's helicopter radio?

"We're going to hover about a hundred Woodland metres from the West Entrance to Pigfrog Command," said Nigel. "Little Else will parachute out and walk the rest of the way. We are also dropping a bundle of linen so that it will appear that she is delivering their washing,"

Arthur Monkberry, standing next to Sodge, leant over and took the handset from him.

"Good luck, chaps! And especially Elsie. If you get into trouble, use your special radio whistle."

Elsie hoped she wouldn't need it.

Half an hour later they were over the dropping zone, and after checking her equipment, Elsie kissed her sister and brother-in-law and jumped bravely out of the helicopter, pulling the rip cord of her parachute, which then plopped open so that she hung comfortably in the air as she made her descent. It was at this moment that she realised once again that, being a fairy, she could have flown down on her own – but, (she supposed), that would have given the game away if she were spotted. In any case, her washerwoman outfit covered her wings so that flying was impossible. She wondered whether this had, in fact, been a wise move. She landed expertly and looked up behind her to see the others waving. She waved back as the helicopter banked to the left and pulled away until it was a tiny dot on the horizon. A tiny *Dot* on the horizon, she thought! She chuckled to herself, and was mildly irritated that there was no-one else around to share her appreciation of her own witty thought about her elder sister.

There was no sound at all. Real snow had fallen overnight, on top of the artificial snow dropped by the Farnsbarneses earlier. It was deep and crisp – and it was even even. She thought it had rather a merry crispness to it. Ha ha! A Merry Crispness, she thought to herself.

But there was serious work to be done. Ergo wasn't even known to be alive – but if he was, she was sure she would find him. She was sad at the same time, for she knew that there was a strong possibility that he had already perished at the hands of the pigfrogs. What a strange word that is, she thought, "perished".

She approached the small side door of Pigfrog Command, which to her seemed dauntingly big. She could just reach the large knocker, which she raised with both hands and let go of, so that it banged down loudly onto the big, wooden door.

A surly-looking pigfrog guard opened an observation window in the door, and grunted "Yes?"

"Washing!" chirped Elsie, breezily.

There was the sound of a bolt being released, and the door crept open with a creak.

"We don't have washing," said the pigfrog, suspiciously. "We like building up a sweat. Nobody washes clothes. They just fall off when they're worn out."

"New orders from your senior commander!" snapped Elsie, in a firm but jolly tone. The pigfrog grunted once more and looked her up and down. If Moundrot really had ordered washing to occur, it would be a foolish guard who stood in the way.

"Alright," he said.

"I have to work in the cells", said Elsie, cleverly. "Would you be so kind as to direct me there?"

The guard rang a bell, and a smaller, slimier guard appeared from down the corridor passage.

"Take this washing lady to the cells, Gritwart!"

"Yes, Corporal."

He lurched back down the corridor, with Elsie walking behind him. It was a wide passage, so that when she quickened her pace to catch him up there was plenty of room for them to walk together, leaving as much room again for other pedestrian traffic coming the other way. Elsie was impressed by the size of the place, and the level of civilisation – although there was a smell in the air that she could have happily done without. Fancy not washing their clothes! But then, they didn't wear much in the way of clothes – it was really more the sweaty body smell that she found a little difficult to ignore. The pigfrog didn't say anything to Elsie. They passed through a work area where a large number of pigfrogs were doing something or other to something or other, and Elsie noticed the vastness of the domed ceiling of the room they were passing through. After about five or ten Woodland minutes, Gritwart stopped and looked down at Little Else.

"Down there, keep walking, first right, keep walking, keep walking, keep walking, second left, stop."

"Thank you so much," said Elsie, not really knowing what else you should say to a pigfrog. Gritwart grunted and slouched off.

Her heart began to pound. Here she was in the middle of the enemy's headquarters, only minutes away from discovering the truth about Ergo and the elf. She took a deep breath and started off again, down the narrower passage which led to the cells. It was then that she noticed something very remarkable. She couldn't quite believe it. As the passageway straightened out, she saw two figures moving towards her. At first, she couldn't make out what they were. They didn't seem to be pigfrogs. One of them was much bigger than the other, and the other – was, well... much smaller than the one that was much bigger than it. As they approached, looking furtively from side to side, she realised...that they were... erm, washerwomen! How? How could the guard have told her there was no washing done in Pigfrog Command, when here were two washerwomen, plain as day. Knowing that real washerwomen would be more likely to see through her disguise, she tried to look as washerwoman-like as possible and kept on walking towards them. As they approached, one of them – the smaller one – muttered a hurried "Good morning, Dear," as they shuffled past.

Elsie kept on going. She didn't want to do anything which would attract attention or delay her from reaching dear Ergo, if indeed he was in a cell. She hurried onwards down the passage, and the two other washerwomen were soon gone, behind her. At least, if washerwomen were a familiar sight in this place, her escape with Ergo dressed as another washerwoman would be easier. She pulled her bundle of clothes, which also contained the washerwoman clothes for Ergo, higher onto her shoulder and quickened her pace towards the cells.

She had by now followed Gritwart's directions all but for the last left turn. Reaching this last corner, she started to follow the passage round to the left. As she turned, she began to hear a groaning sound, together with the growing noise of a commotion in the passage; pigfrog guards shouting orders and running about. She immediately knew she must hide! Whatever the fuss was, it didn't sound as if being a washerwoman would necessarily be a guarantee of safety.

Just then, three huge pigfrogs came hurtling round the corner and knocked her over.

"That's one of them!" shouted the first guard. "That's the small one! The one that didn't bash me with the stone!"

"So the other one must be the one that did, then!" shouted the second guard.

"Brilliant!" said the first one. "Of course it is, you twerp! Run after it – that one must be Quirkhardt, escaping!"

"What about this little one, Sarge?"

"Put it back in the cell and I'll deal with it later!" ordered the Sergeant.

They lifted Elsie, who was too winded and distressed to resist, and dumped her unceremoniously in the very cell from which Ergo and Quirkhardt had just escaped. Oh, no! This wasn't supposed to happen at all!, thought Little Else. The door closed with a loud crangy, banging sound.

Locking her in, the pigfrogs then ran off, presumably after the washerwomen whom she had just passed in the corridor. How strange, thought Little Else.

Chapter Nine: Stairway To Heaven

Ergo heard the commotion, too. Far behind them – or not so far, really – they heard the Sergeant shouting, and Elsie being locked up – but of course they didn't know it was Elsie.

"They must have thought that the real washerwoman was one of us!" said Ergo to Quirkhardt. They were now walking as fast as they could without drawing too much attention to themselves. Ergo, of course, wasn't walking at all. They had devised a way of making him look like a person standing up, by lashing him to one of the "room service" trays with a rope made of straw, knitted together, and standing him on the other tray, which Quirkhardt was dragging along the floor whilst holding Ergo upright with one arm. Not the greatest and most satisfactory impression of a washerwoman, but perhaps it added realism if one washerwoman appeared to be helping the other. What the arrangement was not designed for was being chased.

"Quick! Follow me!" said Quirkhardt, diving into a stairwell. Ergo didn't exactly have much choice, since his new partner was holding him up and dragging him along on the room service tray. He trusted Quirkhardt only because he knew they were both in the same fix, but he knew his natural enemy was only interested in saving his own skin. Until such time as they were both free, he figured that Quirkhardt needed him as much as he needed Quirkhardt. He was a General, after all.

They rushed up the stairs, Ergo using his powerful stomach muscles to push against the stone walls which rose alongside the steps, and Quirkhardt half lifting and half pushing the slug. As they reached the second floor up, they heard the sound of a sizeable pile of guards coming after them, shouting and grunting and narrowing the gap.

"Faster!" implored Ergo, now feeling the sweat running down from the top of his head and across his face. Quirkhardt stretched his stride to two steps at a time.

"This doesn't lead out of this place, does it?" asked Ergo, in between puffing and blowing. He dreaded to hear the answer.

"No, it just seemed like a way of escaping from them," said Quirkhardt.

"So where does it lead?" asked Ergo.

"Just keep climbing," puffed Quirkhardt.

They arrived on the twenty-fourth floor, which was actually still underground. The hordes were about three floors away from them by now. Without even thinking, Quirkhardt threw all his weight against a small door at the other side of the landing. The door burst open.

Ursula stopped playing the piano and looked up, startled. The elf looked amazed. His mouth dropped open.

"Oh, er... Lieutenant Quir... or is it... Sergeant, er..." began Ursula. Quirkhardt was a little surprised that Moundrot's wife would have recognised him, but he realised that his disguise must have slipped a little in the chase. He turned and barred the door with the big wooden bar which hung down at the side, and then swung round to face Ursula.

"Mrs Moundrot, I'm really sorry, but I'm going to have to tie you up," he blurted. With that, he ripped the belt from the elf's trousers and used it to bind Ursula's hands.

"I didn't think my piano playing was that bad!" said Ursula, offended. The elf's trousers fell to the floor around his ankles. His mouth remained open.

The hordes had now reached the door, skidded to a halt, and were now knocking politely on the door which they knew to be the door to their general's quarters.

The elf's mouth was still open. He looked at Ergo. The banging at the door got louder.

"Elf! You're OK! But what happened to Little Else?" asked Ergo, trying to get his breath back.

"She flew away, Ergo – she's a fairy, you know."

"I know she's a flipping fairy," said Ergo, almost offended that the elf would not realise how well he knew Else. "Anyway, that's marvellous news. So she's alright?"

"As far as I know..." began the elf. There were loud shouts at the door.

"Captain – er, Lance Corporal Quirkhardt – er... we know you're in there! Is anybody in there with you? We can't break the door down because the General's not here, but we've sent for him, so you might as well give yourself up! Where is Mrs Moundrot?"

"I'm here..." shouted Ursula, before Quirkhardt could put his hand across her mouth. He gagged her. Ergo and Quirkhardt looked around the room. It was a big, dark pothole and there was no way they could see of getting out of there. And Moundrot was coming up the stairs.

⁓⊱⊰⁓

Elsie was terrified. Here she was in jail in the heart of pigfrog command, Ergo wasn't there. He must be dead, after all. She waited in the half-dark for her captors to come and do to her whatever it was that they did to prisoners who dressed up as washerwomen and broke into their jails. Then she felt hungry, and realised she had her the cheese and mayonnaise sandwich and the flask of tea. Well, she could at least have a little picnic and pretend she was sitting on a lovely grassy bank with Ergo and listening to a beautiful stream flowing by, and the birds singing. So she did. She reached into her bag and found the sandwich, the tea, the dagger and the radio whistle. Oh! The whistle! And the sleep-dagger! She would blow the whistle! But if she blew it now, help might arrive before she had a chance to eat the sandwich. So she waited until she had eaten the sandwich and had a cup of tea before putting the radio whistle to her lips and giving a long, piercing blast.

The blast on the whistle was so loud that Sodge's earphones nearly flew off.

"That's it! That's it! Little Else is in trouble!" he shouted. "Mount up, men!"

The word was passed along from commander to commander, and Arthur's trolls, being the biggest, most awe-inspiring of all the slug allies, formed up at the head of the army, and they all waited until Sodge and Arthur were ready to give the word to attack Pigfrog Command. But Sodge did not have much of a plan. Without Ergo, the slug army was only half the force it had been. Without its leader and strategist the army's morale was low and they simply did not have the power to take Pigfrog Command by force. If they had had, Ergo would have stormed Pigfrog Command in a full frontal attack in the first place. Arthur had already pointed this out to Sodge, but it was only really now that Sodge began to see the truth of it.

He would have to call off any attack, and think hard. Trouble was, thinking was not Sodge's strong point.

Elsie knew she had been a bit optimistic to think that help might arrive before she had finished her sandwich. It even ran through her mind that, had she made herself a bigger sandwich, it would have taken longer to eat it, and the chances of help arriving before she had finished it would have been greater. But, alas, even if she had done that, the help would not have arrived during the picnic. And it would have been more fattening. She looked again at the sleep-dagger. It wasn't really a dagger at all – that was just a name; it was more like a stick that somehow set up vibrations and sent the victim into a lovely sleep, even if you just poked them in the leg with it. Nigel Farnsbarnes really was a clever chap, she thought. Dotty had done well to find him for a husband. He was apt to be a little grumpy and kept bursting into tears, but apart from that he really was rather nice, and a genius, too. She thought for a moment, and decided that it might be a good idea to try the dagger out. If she waited for the pigfrogs to appear, they might search her and take it away from her.

She knew the way out; she only needed to escape from the cell. If she could get out, she could go the rest of the way as a washerwoman; but then – if the pigfrogs that threw her into the cell were chasing other washerwomen, it might not be a safe disguise any more. If she took off the disguise – hey! If she took off the disguise, she'd be a fairy. Admittedly, a fairy with just the basic leotard, ballet shoes and wings, but nevertheless a fairy! Why did she keep forgetting? And fairies can fly! She threw off the washerwoman outfit, and immediately felt better. Why didn't she do this more often? Even her normal tweed suit was a sort of disguise. Something to hide her from the rest of the world. As herself, her real self, she knew she could do almost anything. Elsie felt, at that moment, that her life would somehow be different from now on. She would just be herself, and everything would be alright. She looked out of the big, ceiling-to-floor, barred window, and saw the big shaft that went down into the darker depths where, unbeknown to her, the helicopter was parked – and upwards to the sky, and freedom. If she could only squeeze through the bars, she could fly away; but that wouldn't help Ergo.

Just then, she heard a strange buzzing noise. Well, actually it was a perfectly normal buzzing noise, as buzzing noises go, but it was strange that she should hear one at that moment. She wondered where it could be coming from, so suddenly, until she realised it was from a cell three windows away from her, which, by virtue of the circular shape of the cell block, she could see right into.

"Anybody there?" she asked.

"Funny you should ask that," came the reply, "but yes, actually."

"Who, may I enquire?" Elsie said, politely.

Three faces appeared at the bars of their French window.

They looked like flies, but with friendlier faces than the sort of flies you see on sausage rolls and things. They didn't say anything, but the buzzing sound continued.

"Three flies!" said Elsie.

"Yes, but nice ones," said one of them, slightly paranoidly, and if there's no such word I don't care.

"What are your names?" asked Else.

"The Time Flies!" they chorused.

"I know it does, but what are your names?" asked Little Else.

"No, our name is the Time Flies," said one of them. "We are flies who can travel through time, that's why we are called the Time Flies. That is why we wear these tight shiny costumes, because we are able to do very special things by entering the Time Warp Drive and travelling around to fight evil."

Elsie couldn't quite believe it, but it was indeed less silly-sounding than magnetism and electricity and whatever else. Their costumes certainly were tight and shiny, and they looked rather like those funny little characters you see on cereal packets, but better.

"Pleased to meet you," she said, feeling rather foolish, "but why are you in this pigfrog jail?"

"We don't know, we just arrived in our time travels," said the Main Fly. "But what is this about a pigfrog jail? Trust us to land in a jail when we just set out for a Sunday afternoon random spin through the past. We like random – it's very exciting and you never now where you'll end up. And by the way, what year is it?"

"Well, I'm not sure, exactly," said Elsie, "but it is apparently somewhere between the Olden Days and last week."

"Wow!" chorused the Time Flies. "Far Out! And these pigfrog things – what's the story?"

Elsie told them the whole story. They couldn't believe it – but then it was less silly than travelling through time.

"Wow!" they said. Elsie noticed that they said it rather a lot.

"The thing is," said Elsie, "I don't know what happened about half an hour ago, just before I was captured and thrown in this cell. I have a feeling that two washerwomen were in here, and I think I saw them escaping, but I don't know anything about how or why and I think it might be important. And most importantly, I don't know where my friend, Ergo is."

"I see," said the Main Fly. "Well, we can easily tell you what happened in this cell an hour ago. We just jump back into our Time Thimble..."

"Your what?" asked Elsie, incredulously.

"Our Time Thimble," said the Main Fly. "It is the thing that actually does the transporting of us, through time."

"Oh," said Elsie.

"You know, a thimble, but converted. By us. To fly through time."

"Of course," said Elsie.

The flies jumped into the thimble, said goodbye to Elsie and were gone. Just like that. Amazing, really.

When the flies snapped through into an hour earlier, they still had a view of Elsie's cell, but in it were a slug, half-dressed as a washerwoman, being tied to a tray by another thing - Quirkhardt, as it happened – also in a dress. The Time Flies were well-travelled and had seen a lot of strange things in their time, but this did give them cause for concern. They watched, transfixed, as Ergo and Quirkhardt transformed themselves into two very passable washerwomen, and saw Ergo removing Quirkhardt's leg irons by greasing the pigfrog's ankles with pigswill and the goo from the walls, and pulling like mad. The slug seemed to be the one with the brains. The flies saw them crouch by the door, saw the guard enter – saw Quirkhardt bash the Sergeant guard with a big stone – and saw them make their escape. As the two intrepid escapers made their way out of the cell and down the corridor, the Time Flies flew behind them and watched the entire scenario as they passed Elsie in the corridor and then fled up the stairs to the room where they now were, followed and trapped by their pigfrog pursuers.

As General Moundrot began to thump his way up the stairs towards his quarters, the Time Flies returned to Elsie and jumped an hour ahead, so that when they appeared before her, in their thimble – this time in her cell – it seemed that almost no time had passed at all.

The flies told Elsie the whole story.

"So Ergo is alive! Hip, Hip, Hooray!" shouted Elsie. "And everything's going to be alright!"

"Well, yes, but the old General is just about now arriving at the top of the stairs, and he isn't in a very good mood," said the Main Fly.

Elsie didn't care. She just knew everything would be alright.

"Can't you fly an hour ahead in time and see what happens next?" pleaded Elsie.

"Cheating!" they all shouted merrily in unison. They had obviously been asked that before. "That spoils everything, and in any case, would you really want to see it if it is not good news? Hope is the thing that carries you through these times. If you saw bad news it would make it difficult for you to do all the things you need to do to keep fighting for what you want. You are the one who makes things happen."

"Ooh, dear," thought Elsie, "that's a bit deep!" But she knew they were right.

"Ok, then – but listen, guys," said Elsie, slipping into their slang language, "if Ergo and the elf and this fairly friendly pigfrog thing are all trapped in the chief pigfrog's cave, can't we get out and go and rescue them?" She thought for a moment.

The Time Flies had described to her that Moundrot's room had a shaft of light which penetrated from the top of the mountain, down at an oblique angle, into the roof of his bathroom. At certain times of the day it made rather a nice prism and rainbow effect on the bathroom floor. He and Ursula never had a bath, so never used the bathroom, but they had had one installed as a status symbol (it was the only bathroom in Pigfrog Command), and Ursula had felt that it would enhance the property's resale value.

"Well, we can try, but what about you?" said the Main Fly.

"Can you tell me your names so that I don't have to keep thinking of you as the Main Fly, Second Main Fly and so on?" said Little Else, not wanting to say

"Least Important Fly", in case of giving offence to the poor least important one.

"Oh, sorry," said the Main Fly. Yes – my name is Malcolm, this is Malcolm, and this is Malcolm."

"Oh, no!" said Elsie. "Why are you all called Malcolm?"

"Just a coincidence," said the main Malcolm. "It does get rather confusing, I admit. We call each other Malcolm One, Malcolm Two and Malcolm Three."

"Ah, that's better," said Elsie. "Anyway, look. I think I may be able to squeeze through the bars of my French windows now that I don't have my washerwoman outfit on."

"Go on, then," urged Malcolm Two.

She walked over to the window and applied herself determinedly to one of the gaps, breathing in and squeezing hard. She had discarded her bag, but held the sleep-dagger in her hand, so as not to leave it behind. To her great delight, and with a slurpy sort of plop, she popped out onto the ledge beyond, a free fairy once again, resplendent in leotard, ballet shoes and wings.

"Hip, Hip, Hooray!" she said. The Time Flies agreed.

"Bravo!" buzzed Malcolm Three, limply.

"Right, well, let's get on with it!" Little Else cried, and launched herself off the ledge of the window, the flying sensation giving her a renewed sense of achievement.

"Let's find that skylight shaft into the chief pigfrog's room!"

The Time Flies leapt into the air, too. Malcolm Three had the Time Thimble (which was bigger than him) strapped to his back, and the four adventurers flew upwards to the distant daylight.

Quirkhardt quivered as Moundrot bashed on the door.

"Quirkhardt, you snivelling clot! Open this door or when we get in by breaking it down I'll mince you slowly from the feet upwards over a period of a three years!" Even Moundrot had to stop for a second to contemplate and appreciate the idea. It was one of his best. He bashed on the door.

"And don't think holding my wife as a hostage is going to work. You can have her! I was thinking of getting rid of her anyway." He smirked, in the certain knowledge that it would not come to that – but knowing how much it would hurt Ursula to hear it. He actually did sort of love her, and anyway, she kept him company in the hibernation, and had a very nice pair of gooey, scaly, fat legs to lean against when he slept. Ursula was, indeed, mortified and horrified to hear her Jim being so horrible.

"MMMHHggHMMMM!!" she protested, through the gag.

Ergo felt sorry for her. She was only a poor sowfrog who had fallen in with the wrong type. Mind you, she had probably enjoyed the spoils of success, he thought. She had probably kept quiet while Moundrot did his snarling despot act, and kicked everybody around, while she sat there and had her room service and her piano lessons. Maybe she even liked the idea of being married to a violent killer who was nice to her occasionally. Maybe she deserved this. But maybe not. He hoped not. He was an optimist. He hoped she was nice, really. (He was right and wrong – sometimes she was nice, and sometimes she wasn't – just like you and me. Well, you, anyway).

All of Ergo's thoughts, described above, flashed past in less time than it has taken you to read them. In a flash, he dropped to the floor, and using the strong stomach muscles of which he was so proud, he crawled over to the window which looked out across the front entrance of Pigfrog Command. He could see the snow, and the ground sloping away to the right, where Carol Singing Squad Number One had first dealt with Corporal Flighnever, in self-defence (although Ergo was not aware of the particular pigfrog's name). He deduced that his army must be out there, wondering where he was and whether he was alive.

"I've told them we're alive," chipped in the elf, intuitively knowing what Ergo was thinking.

"How did you know I was thinking about that?" said Ergo.

"I'm an elf!" said Horace. "My name is Horace, by the way."

"I think 'the elf' is nicer," said Ergo, cruelly.

"Oh," said the elf, deflated. "I quite like the name."

"Sorry," said Ergo. "Yes, it is a nice name. I was just trying to make a joke about it. I do that. It's a very bad habit. I'm sorry. What can elves do, then?" he added. "Apart from knowing what people are thinking?"

"Not a lot. Play the piano. We're quite good at crosswords. Knitting, that kind of thing."

"What, no magic or things like that?" said Ergo.

"Some of the clever ones are good at Bridge, and others are able to turn people into handsome princes," said Horace, as if the latter was about as clever as the former. Certainly, in Horace the Elf's eyes, playing bridge was just as useful, and could be used more often.

"Are you lot coming out or are we coming in?" barked Moundrot through the door, the bass frequencies of his voice drumming up through the doorposts and around the walls.

"Get knotted, you fat, slimy old scumbag!" shouted Quirkhardt, in the bravest, most liberated and enjoyable moment of his life. If he was going to be minced from the feet upwards he might as well enjoy it.

"Aaaghrrummmppphhhh!" thundered Moundrot as he threw his entire weight against the door – but the door did not give way, as he himself had designed the bar which bolted it from within. He once again launched himself, with all his angry weight, against the strong door and this time, with a splintering sound, one of its planks split down the middle, so that he could now see into the room. The crack was, however, too slim for a hand to get through and unbolt the door.

As Moundrot braced himself for another crushing charge, Ergo was rushing around the room for a suitable exit, which he was not hopeful of finding.

Ursula slipped her gag off.

"The bathroom!" she shouted.

So she was a good 'un after all! Good old Ursula! Why – we don't know. Probably because Jim had been so nasty to her, and in any case she couldn't stand to see blood all over her carpet. Goo, yes. But blood, no thanks. She was a lady. There were limits. Whatever the reason, she had given Ergo the tip he needed. He pushed himself into the bathroom, and came in sight of the shaft of light and hope which shone down at him.

"Flipping heck! Look at this! There's a shaft leading up to the daylight! Come on, Horace! Come on, Lance Corporal Thingy!"

Quirkhardt was livid to be addressed as "Lance Corporal" by a slug, but delighted to be given the chance to live. Livid and delighted, he hurtled past Ergo and was first up through the skylight, beginning to shin his way up the narrow shaft, not really caring whether Ergo and the elf followed him or not. In a way, he hoped that they wouldn't, so that Moundrot would catch them and spend precious minutes of Quirkhardt-escape-time ripping them limb from limb – except that Ergo didn't have any limbs, so that would have been alright.

Ergo stood back and helped the piano-elf up through the skylight. It was big enough for Quirkhardt, so it was easily big enough for Horace and Ergo. They scrambled in, just as the door shattered and Moundrot fell into the room at Ursula's feet.

"Where did they go?" demanded Moundrot. "Rubbtrubniggrabbad-rotasoppa!" said Ursula, cunningly pretending to be momentarily insane. What a lovely lady she was! Well, not exactly lovely, but a nice person.

"The skylight in the bathroom!" shouted Moundrot. He was no fool! He bounded, in a middle-aged-to-old sort of way, into the thus-named room and missed Ergo's vanishing slug-tail by about a Woodland second.

"Damn! Damn and Double-Blithering Goo-Gobs!" cursed Moundrot.

Undaunted, he pushed himself up the shaft and found that he fitted nicely. He reminded himself that he must tell his tailor, so that his ceremonial uniforms could be cut to the measurement of the shaft. He forced himself onwards. Ergo was only about two Woodland metres from him, and he knew he was faster than a stupid slug. He was, by now, frothing at the mouth and laughing in a really horrible way, like somebody who might be about to step on a ladybird, but a lot worse. Or somebody who has won a lot of money on the Lottery and is going to spend it all on chips. His dribbling got wetter and

louder as he reached Ergo in the tunnel, and he grabbed forward and just managed to catch his slippery tail as it wriggled frantically away from him. Ergo stopped with a jolt.

"Oh, No!"

To be caught in the spiny paws of his arch enemy, and soon to be ripped limb from limb – well, in a manner of speaking. What a terrible fate! His life flashed before him and he thought, finally, of Little Else – beautiful Little Else, his very own fairy, who didn't, and would never know about his passion for her. He was going to die here, in a pothole shaft, miles from home, at the hands of a pigfrog, just like Elsie's brother. He didn't so much mind for himself, but the grief Elsie would go through would be terrible. He hoped. Oh, what guilt to hope she would be stricken with grief! Maybe she wouldn't feel sad or anything at all. That would be better in a way, but worse in every other way than the way he first meant. Oh! Blithering, smelly rotten slimy bits! Goodbye, World! Goodbye, Don't Be So Ridiculous Valley. Goodbye, middle sized mates. Goodbye, George Formby records. But his main thoughts were that he had never been brave enough to talk properly to Little Else. He was brave enough in battle, but to talk frankly to Else, that was another matter. He was a coward. Oh, to die a coward!

Moundrot tightened his grip and pulled Ergo backwards and downwards. It hurt.

Hang on a minute, thought Ergo. This shaft is getting narrower. If I could only get a bit higher I reckon the slimy old bounder would get stuck. With a burst of adrenalin – yes, slugs do have it (tick it off in your *I-Spy Book Of Slug Body Chemicals*, for forty points) – he pulled upwards, helped by his slime, and the General – I mean the other General, momentarily lost his grip. Ergo seized his chance and capitalised on his opportunity, which just about amounts to the same thing, and leapt upwards in the shaft, with the elf ahead of him, complaining that Ergo was forcing the pace, and Quirkhardt way up ahead, nearly at the entrance.

Moundrot grabbed again, this time using one of his sharp claws, which penetrated Ergo's sensitive bottom area and caused him to let out a great cry of pain, pleasing Moundrot no end. Moundrot pulled Ergo towards him and opened his huge, grinning, dribbling jaws, so that he could crunch down on his torso and rip him in half.

"You can have the piano!" shouted Ergo to the elf, in a last, unselfish gesture of unselfishness.

"It's mine already!" shouted the elf, not realising the delicacy of the situation, and therefore appearing a tiny bit insensitive.

Moundrot's jaws closed, cutting through Ergo's flesh, and hurting like hell. Ergo responded by twitching his main body area upwards so that it slithered out of Moundrot's nasty thrashing gob to safety, leaving only the tip of his tail in between Moundrot's sharp and desperate teeth. Just at that moment Moundrot stopped abruptly. The tunnel had become too narrow, and he was stuck fast. Ergo continued upwards.

"Double-Blithering Goo-Gobs, and then some!" yelled Moundrot, dropping the tail piece from his jaws, so that it landed on his shoulder, where he could no longer reach it, as he was stuck fast in the shaft. Ergo couldn't see all this, as he was forcing himself upwards, using his highly developed and Very-Attractive-To-Girl-Slugs-But-Unfortunately-Not-Fairies-He-Thought stomach muscles, and gaining height and distance away from the cursing pigfrog general who stayed stuck by the force of his own bulk, in the ever-narrowing skylight-shaft of his own bathroom.

As he reached the top, Quirkhardt just managed to clear the sides and leapt out jubilantly. He had known he would clear the width at the top, as he had only a week before supervised a working party in the shaft, and had personally entered the shaft from the top. This had been necessary in order to prove to the soon-to-become late-lamented Corporal Flighnever that it was not difficult to fit a pipe over the top so that essence of dead-slug-body-goo could be injected into Moundrot's quarters to stimulate his supreme commander's thrill-buds while he slept through the off-season for slug- squashing, before the September Awakening.

That was only a week ago, mind. The thought seemed impossible. Now he was an enemy of the pigfrog nation – an outcast, and his once-beloved or at least respected and feared general wanted to mince him slowly from the feet up. Such was army life! Maybe another week and he might be back as a guest at Ursula Moundrot's sherry parties. Hmmm. Not a lot of realistic hope of that. Still, you never knew.

Like Ergo's thoughts earlier, these thoughts were rapid, and went gushing through Quirkhardt's selfish, cowardly and idiotic brain in a flash of a split

Woodland second.

He contemplated squashing the elf. He also thought it might be fun to squash Ergo, now that he no longer needed him to be the brains of the escape. As he was thinking about it, the Time Flies and Little Else appeared out of the sky and flew down towards him. Summoning up all her courage, and hoping the sleep-dagger really was only a sleep-dagger, for she had never tested it, Elsie drew level with Quirkhardt and stabbed him gently, sensitively. And in a ladylike manner. She had taken him for a nasty, smelly pigfrog – which he was – not recognising him as a semi-friendly one, since his washerwoman outfit was now in tatters, and his dribbling, horrid pigfrog characteristics were plain for all to see.

Quirkhardt fell into a sweet, dream-infested sleep, landing with a thud on the ground where he had stood as he had been trying to decide whether or not to give Ergo a right good squashing. Serve him right. Nasty piece of work. His mother had loved him once, but even she had given up all hope by the time he had reached the age of three. Anyway, he was asleep now, so everything was alright.

Ergo emerged from the shaft.

"Oh, flipping, flopping slimy bits!" he said, falling down exhausted (to the extent that, being slug, he wasn't already down), on the slushy, snowy, semi-grassy mountainside.

Little Else fluttered down to him like an Angel. She took his soft head in her hands and raised it as he slept, to her lips. She kissed it, slowly and lovingly. She moved her hands down until she was caressing his middle bit, and hugging him warmly. She put her head on his heaving, tired, slug-version-of-manly chest.

"Ergo," she whispered, "you are my beautiful hero. My heart is yours forever, and I wish we could get married."

"Pardon?" said Ergo, who had been half asleep. "What did you say, Elsie... er... uh... Elsie! Haha! It's really you! I thought I was dreaming, and I was half way through my song where I sing "Thinking About Little Else" and playing the piano after several very serious music lessons from Horace the Extremely Clever Piano-Teaching Elf, at the Don't Be So Ridiculous Valley Academy Of Music."

"Yes, it's really me, Ergo, and it seems that the pigfrog that was following you up the shaft is stuck there, and the one that came out first is fast asleep, due to an experimental but very necessary stab from my sleep-dagger, invented by Nigel Farnsbarnes, patented somewhere between the Olden Days and last week, more like last week!"

"Oh, Joy!" shouted Ergo. "But what were you saying just now? Could you say it with me listening? Sorry about that!"

Little Else paused, rather irritatedly. She hated it when men didn't listen. It was disrespectful. What a way to start a relationship! But than, Ergo was a great general and probably had his mind on higher things – and anyway, he had been asleep.

"Oh, I've forgotten."

" You said that he is your beautiful hero and you wish you could get married and your heart is his forever," said Quirkhardt, who appeared to have woken up.

"How did you know that?" asked Ergo, impressed but slightly miffed that Quirkhardt had known before he had.

"I was only pretending to be asleep," admitted Quirkhardt. "That thing's no good. Maybe the battery has run out."

Elsie was both deflated at the news that her sleep-dagger was a dud, and elated that someone had remembered her speech, because she didn't think she would ever be able to remember it herself, let alone have the courage to deliver it when Ergo was listening. It had been easy when she had known he was asleep. But what would Ergo think of her now that she had told him openly what her true thoughts were?

Ergo was too moved to talk. He didn't want to burst into tears in front of the fairy he loved, and who apparently thought of him as a bit of a hero. What if she saw him crying and changed her mind about the hero bit? He wasn't worldly enough to know that to show his true emotions could only endear him to her even more, and that to hold them in was weaker and, er, not as strong.

Holding back his tears, he looked at her for a while, then said, "Oh, Little

Else, I've dreamed about you – sorry it's a soppy thing to say, but even generals can be soppy sometimes, especially if they are me. I have wanted to hug you and hold you and be with you and wash your back in the bath since I first set eyes on you, but of course I didn't think it would be appropriate then, and by the way, this doesn't mean that I think your back is at all dirty in any way."

"Don't be daft, my beautiful – well, fairly beautiful – Ergo! Now you are alive and well and free from the evil pigfrogs – always assuming they don't come round that hill and kill us or something – which I bet you a Woodland shilling they don't – and we can be together for as long as we like, and you can wash my back whenever you want to – even if it isn't dirty, which is often the case."

"Oh, how barbaric!" said Quirkhardt, who was genuinely disgusted at the thought of two people washing each other, or washing at all. It didn't seem to fit his pigfrog ethic of sweat and odour being right and proper and just plain natural.

A small tear appeared on his lower eyelid, and trickled down across his scaly, ugly, officer-material face, and dropped off his inadequate chin onto his vest. "You know," he began, "somehow I don't think I was cut out to be a nasty, aggressive pigfrog. It doesn't seem to suit my bio-rhythms or something, and I'm a Virgo, so it just doesn't fit into my natural way of doing things. It goes against the grain, in a sort of spiritual way – perhaps that's why I'm such a failure,"

Nigel had joined in crying by now, but Nigel's crying was serious crying. (By the way, Dotty and Nigel had landed in the blue-at-the-moment helicopter, during Elsie's first speech.) Nigel was in a right state, crying and wailing into his pocket handkerchief, which, incidentally, was a special clockwork one. It was quite embarrassing even for Elsie, whose moment it was, and who should have been expected to tolerate any displays of emotion, however excessive.

"My tail hurts like blinking blithery," said Ergo, not wanting to use stronger language in front of the fairy sisters, and sounding

a little twee as a result.

Oh, these are my new friends, the Time Flies, by the way," said Elsie to Ergo. "They are flies who fly through time, hence the name and the tight costumes. Time Flies – Ergo, Ergo, Time Flies."

"Pleased to meet you," said the three Malcolms, in unison.

"And pleased to be met by you," said Ergo. "So you fly through time, eh? What's it like?" He felt it was a bit of a silly, nerdish question, but then he couldn't think of anything else to say. In any case, before they could answer, he remembered his injured tail. He could live without it, but then again, he'd rather not. Didn't see why he should, *actually*.

"I wonder if the old villain is still down there," said Ergo, knowing that the tail piece would have dropped out of Moundrot's mouth during the howling that followed his getting stuck, and that it would be very unlikely to have got past his fat body to drop further down the shaft. "They can sew things like that back on again these days, you know," he said, with a knowledgeable look on his face, followed by a wince of pain. It was his flipping tail, after all! He would go back down and get it! What a flipping cheek to bite it off! He would soon show the old pigfrog what he thought about that!

"Dot, be a dear and tie me to the helicopter, would you?"

"No, no, no!" said Malcolm One. "Leave it to us! Not wishing to be presumptuous, but this is just up our street!"

Without a word, the Time Flies took to the air and were soon down the dark shaft and back again, having lifted the missing piece of sluggy flesh right off Moundrot's shoulder, as he gasped and grunted and cursed.

"Here, you are Sir! Your bit of bottom, back again, good as new!"

"It's not my bottom, *actually*," said Ergo, with as much dignity as he could muster. "It's my tail – quite a different piece of the body with a totally different function. But thanks heaps for getting it."

He gratefully took the tail fragment and put it in Elsie's tea flask (which was, after all, half his now, if they were getting married). Married! Wow! To Elsie – Little Else! She had mentioned it, hadn't she? A bit forward, mind. But he cared not a tiny little jot about Elsie's forwardness, without which he would never have dared to even hope she might be, you know... well, well... you know.

"Come on, then! Let's get back to the troops!" said Ergo, regaining his leadership qualities.

"What about me?" said Quirkhardt, rather pathetically. Ergo looked at him, for the first time in daylight. He was sitting on the snow, looking very sorry for himself.

"Well, you can come, too, but no funny business or else!" said Ergo.

There was still a very real danger that Moundrot might be rescued quickly from below by his soldiers, or that the pigfrogs who had pursued them up the stairs might be intelligent enough to work out that they were escaping through the ventilation shaft and go round to try to cut them off. In fact, the more Ergo thought about it, the more it seemed certain that this was about to happen.

They resolved to move quickly away from the area, skirt around a small mountain peak and down through a gully which the Time Flies and Elsie had explored from the air and identified as a good route back to the waiting slug army.

When they arrived at Sodge's position they were greeted with loud cheering from the slugs, squirreloids, gnome-adds and trolls who comprised the slug force. They had been about to storm the place, which would have been the worst possible thing to have done, but all they could think of.

"It is a bit galling," said Sodge. "It's lovely to see you, and all that, Ergo, but we feel a bit as if we haven't exactly *done* anything."

"I know," said Ergo. "We've had all the fun, but then it is important that some people don't get quite as much fun as others so that the ones having the fun can feel that they are having more fun than the first lot." This wasn't a particularly convincing or grateful comment, but Sodge took it in good spirit.

Ergo guessed that after the terrible beating that Third Battalion had experienced, it was improbable that the pigfrogs would launch a full frontal attack on his main slug force (which, of course was not all slugs, as I have said, but was called the slug army because it had been their idea). Ergo was right. The pigfrogs spent the rest of the day pulling their esteemed general from the ventilation shaft and being nice to him. Moundrot lay in the bath for the first time ever, and soaked away some of his sorrows. Major Accuppa organised the general's dinner, followed by a huge glass of brandy and a large chocolate cigar.

Ergo's army set off for home and arrived three days later, unchallenged by any pigfrog forces, and with Private Quirkhardt as their prisoner.

"This isn't the last they'll hear from us," said Ergo. "After all, we said we'd wipe them out, and we haven't yet. What's more, they've got our piano and Nige's helicopter. And the real Christmas is coming soon".

"Oh, yes, so it is," said Sodge, without any particular feeling of excitement.

Next Chapter: On with the Story

It was a beautiful cold, sunny morning on the edge of Don't Be So Ridiculous Valley, and the trees basked in that sort of sideways sunlight you get when the sun is low. Across the flat ground that sloped away from the valley (which was actually a hill, don't forget), there came the muted but clear sound of hammering, and of voices busily talking in the cold air. A soft, blue mist hung lazily over the river and outwards across the few houses and cottages that, provided you were looking at them, would lead the eye up towards the Farnsbarneses' tree house, situated some distance beyond, where the Woodlands began again. If you weren't looking at them, this didn't happen.

There was a furtive atmosphere as squirreloid cart-pushers and slugs-on-wheels rushed between workers nailing and screwing, hammering and sawing. The trolls were the most efficient workers, the slugs the least efficient, for fairly obvious physical reasons, but in case you haven't been concentrating, the trolls had huge, muscular arms that hung down to the ground, and the slugs were just a tiny bit limbless. They did try, though.

Nigel and Ergo were conferring together over at the side of the trunk of the tree house.

"Gosh, Ergo, I'm so flipping pleased with myself I can hardly speak," said Nigel.

"Yes, well, you've done a wonderful job designing this lot," said Ergo, with genuine gratitude. "How long do you think it might be before it's all finished?"

"Well, not including painting, I'd say about another two days," said Nige.

"Great," said Ergo. "I'll tell Sodge to stand by to get the lads to start moving all the kit over from the camp site."

He stood back and looked at the partly-constructed extensions to the tree-house. Nigel had done a very good job; Ergo hadn't just been saying it to be

The Tree House Barracks

nice. Fourteen wooden blocks of accommodation for the chaps had been built, radiating away from the back of the tree trunk, and at the front, just below the balcony where the Large Disused Owl often sat, there was a headquarters building which had everything including one of those invalid chairlifts that goes up the bannisters, so that Ergo could get from floor one to two to three when he didn't have his wheels on, without it taking half an hour. There was also a jail, which had been built first, to house Quirkhardt while they tried to think of what to do to him.

They couldn't kill him. Firstly, that would have pleased Moundrot, and they wouldn't want that. Secondly, it would have been emotionally too difficult to do. What would you do, stab him at point blank range when he wasn't looking? Of course not. Ergo reflected that it was far easier (even fun) to kill pigfrogs who were a long way off, but almost impossible when you sort of knew them a bit. In any case, Quirkhardt and he had escaped from jail together. It seemed a bit rude just to kill him. In addition to all these reasons, the fact was that Quirkhardt kept saying he was sorry. Probably lying, thought Ergo, but you never knew.

That evening there was a huge barbecue to celebrate Ergo and Elsie's engagement. Ergo brought out his George Formby records and everybody danced around. The Time Flies were enjoying themselves (as it does when you are) and drinking quite a lot. Even Quirkhardt was let out for the evening on his promise to be sociable and help give out the salads.

❧

Quirkhardt was a confused pigfrog. He was in the captivity of these nasty slippery little blighters who were treating him quite well and, because of his adventure escaping with Ergo, he had gained a sneaking respect for the slug commander, quite against his normal malicious and begrudging nature. At the same time, he had, through fear and from the treatment he had received from Moundrot, developed a feeling about the pigfrog General which wasn't far away from loathing. In fact it was in the same place as loathing, because loathing was exactly what it was. Minced from the feet upwards, indeed! The balls of Quirkhardt's feet began to ache whenever he saw something nasty like blood, or thought about painful things. He didn't know why, it just happened. The thought of being minced made the balls of his feet feel really horrible, and he shivered, like you do when you feel all horrible all of a sudden. Yeauucch!

He snapped out of those thoughts, and carried on giving out the salads with as much of a polite smile as he could fake. Giving out salads to slugs and trolls and gnome-adds was not his idea of an evening out, but it was better than being minced.

Now the George Formby records had stopped and there was a band playing. Lanterns swung on the gentle breeze, and a happy atmosphere warmed the tree house barracks gardens. Squirreloids and other woodland thingies were chattering away, enjoying themselves. At one table sat Nigel, Dotty and Little Else, enjoying the smell of the Breakfast Woodsmoke which Dotty had sprayed around the garden despite the fact that it was evening.

Horace the piano elf had formed the small orchestra with himself on piano, two of Carol Singing Squad Number One (or was it Carol Singing Squad Number One?) on backing vocals, a gnome-add called Mr Clarke on a sort of Woodland saxophone, constructed from a piece of rubber tubing and a soup ladle, and a large girl slug called Smorl played bass.

Suddenly, as a special surprise, a different band marched in and played a rousing fanfare, written especially by Horace for the occasion. This was the Don't Be So Ridiculous Valley Marching Wind Band, who were proudly sponsored by the DBSRV Academy Of Music. The band was made up of various woodland creatures, slugs and oddball humanoid and other characters. Everyone was welcome in the DBSRV Marching Wind Band. One of them had a proper saxophone, which made Mr Clarke jealous, but as the proper saxophone player also had what looked like a gherkin for a nose Mr Clarke was only a very tiny bit jealous of his saxophone. "Noses are more important than saxophones," thought Mr Clarke to himself, wisely. Some of the band players were slugs playing mouth organs. They were conducted by a very talented-looking ginger squirrel wearing a golden sherriff's badge. Their extended fanfare acted as a perfect introduction for Ergo to get up and say something.

Ergo took a position where he could best be seen and began to address his friends. They became silent as he spoke.

"Dear friends and lovely, smashing, delightful comrades-at-arms," he began.

"Speak for yourself!" shouted Sodge, like one of those people who shout

out merrily during speeches at weddings and things.

"Well, when I say arms you know what I mean," said Ergo, wiggling his knobbly bits to make the point. Everybody laughed, not because it was funny, but because they were happy and wanted to laugh anyway.

"This is the happiest day of my life," he continued. "Well, actually, yesterday was quite happy. And the day I first discovered chewing gum was quite good, too. But this, is certainly in the top three happy days I've ever known, and it's not yet even finished, so it could get better, and is highly unlikely to get worse."

Elsie blushed. She knew that she was the cause of this being in the top three happy days of Ergo's life, and it made her happy, too. She was pleased that the candlelight made it impossible for the others to see her blushing.

"And the cause of my state of extreme happiness, the like of which I have rarely known, is sitting not a million miles from just over there!" announced Ergo, swishing his right knobbly bit out towards Little Else, in the manner of a show business host introducing somebody at a concert. There was a huge round of applause, thumping of tables, and cheering. Elsie began to cry, just a little bit, in a lovely sort of way, not like you do when you fall off your bike, but more like when you get a nice letter from somebody you like and haven't seen for ages.

"And furthermore," added Ergo, "I would like to say that this beautiful and brave fairy who has foolishly agreed to become my wife, is the nicest person I have ever, ever met and that if she got any nicer it just wouldn't be fair on everyone else, which it isn't anyway, because she's already nicer than you could imagine – not, that everybody else in the garden doesn't come a very close equal second!"

Speech making wasn't Ergo's strongest point, but they all clapped and cheered again, and Elsie stood up and held out her hands to stop the applause.

"I know it's not usual for the bride – or future bride – to make a speech," she said, "but I just wanted to say..." (she sniffed back a tear) "that Ergo and I are going to try very hard and the fact that he's a slug and I'm a fairy won't make the slightest difference – except that dancing will be rather difficult!" There were more roars of happiness from everybody.

From his position over on the edge of the garden, Quirkhardt watched and listened in a not-very-interested-but-not-nasty-either sort of way. Now that the band had stopped playing, and the voices were some distance from him, he heard very clearly when somebody or something gave out a sound like "Psssst" from the bushes behind him. It might have been "Hssst", but whatever it was, it was somebody trying to catch his attention. He looked around. He could see nothing.

"Quirkhardt!" whispered the voice, loudly.

It knew his name! Something in the bushes knew his name! He decided to ignore it, thinking it might be his imagination – forgetting that he didn't have one (although imagining that he did have).

Ergo and Elsie were still making speeches, or rather, Arthur Monkberry was now proposing a toast to the engaged couple, holding up a wooden goblet full of a frothing concoction which looked like Tizer and shaving foam all mixed up together.

"Pssst, Quirkhardt!" came the voice, again. This time he knew he was not imagining it. He stepped slowly backwards towards the place from where the voice had come. He had no reason to be afraid of it – it sounded quite friendly. As he got nearer the bushes, a great big hand darted out and grabbed him by the apron (which he was wearing for giving out the salads) and pulled him violently into the bushes.

"Ssssh..." said the voice. It was a pigfrog voice! Quirkhardt made a decision that he was afraid after all. "Don't be afraid!" said the voice. Quirkhardt didn't obey.

"I'll be afraid if I like!" said Quirkhardt, indignantly.

"There's no need," said Major Accuppa.

"Major Accuppa! Erm, what a nice surprise, er... Sir," stammered

Quirkhardt, not now knowing his own rank since it had been so much reduced, but knowing that the Major was his superior officer whatever the case.

"Listen, Quirkhardt," whispered Accuppa. "Moundrot is very cross indeed with you, my lad."

"Well yes, I know..." said Quirkhardt, thinking that it had been rather an obvious statement on Accuppa's part.

"And he has sent me to give you a message. Knowing that I am a nice, kind, gentle, non-fighting pigfrog, and more used to dishing out the finest pigswill in the land, and expecting that you would not be too frightened of me, he chose me to bear the message to you. If he had wanted just to kill you he would have sent somebody more, er... normal."

Quirkhardt didn't believe it. He still thought it was a trick of some sort.

"OK, what have you come to tell me then?" asked Quirkhardt, his curiosity becoming stronger than his fear.

"Moundrot says that if you prove to him that your only crime is that you are a stupid, good-for-nothing, idle, smelly, ugly, weak, cowardly idiot, but still loyal to his command, he will reinstate you to your former rank and let Ursula put you back on the invitation list for her sherry parties. But you will have to become a spy – gain the confidence of their leader and the other slug enemies, and help to bring about their extermination by our army. You must gather information and send it back to us, and then perform a deed which will regain the trust of your General – kill their leader's pretty little fairy lady friend!"

"What, and then I won't get minced, you mean?" asked Quirkhardt, rather too quickly to retain any real negotiating dignity.

"Well, he would hardly re-promote you to Captain and then mince you, would he?"

111

Quirkhardt wasn't so sure. He knew Moundrot. Mincing a Captain would probably give him more pleasure than mincing a Private or a Lance Corporal. Still, he was interested in the deal. He really didn't have much to lose, as he didn't know what the slugs might do to him soon anyway.

"What does he want me to find out?" asked Quirkhardt.

"Anything of use... of course, their strength, their numbers... details of their weapons – particularly those exploding hat things – what they eat, what they don't eat, what they like, what they dislike, their favourite colours, stuff like that."

A delighted little twisty bit appeared at the edge of former Captain Quirkhardt's mouth. This would be easy – and fun. It would reinstate him within the pigfrog army with at least his former rank, and he would be invited to Ursula Moundrot's sherry parties. The only thing he didn't really have the stomach for was squashing or otherwise bringing about the premature death of Little Else. Firstly, he had grown to like her in a disliking kind of a way, and thirdly, he wasn't very brave. There was no second reason.

"OK, I'll do it, Major," announced Quirkhardt, as if it had been a decision requiring thought.

"Good, Quirkhardt," said Accuppa. "And as a gesture, Moundrot has kindly authorised me to promote you immediately to the rank of Lance Corporal! But remember... if you fail, he will show no mercy. I'll meet you here again in exactly one week from now, for your first report."

With that, Accuppa was gone, and Lance Corporal Quirkhardt was free to choose his moment to creep nonchalantly out of the bushes so as to avoid suspicion.

The party went on until four o'clock in the morning, and Ergo danced with Little Else by standing on a tea tray converted by Nigel, with castor wheels on the bottom, so that she could twirl him around as the band played. The stars twinkled and the trees swayed in the breeze. The moon glowed. Everyone was happy.

Quirkhardt brooded with satisfaction upon the prospect that their happiness would not last for very long, and gave out the salads with an ever more polite smile.

Another Chapter

The Large Disused Owl coughed loudly and opened the *Woodland Daily Trumpet*. There was more to him than met the eye. He was a grumpy old soul with an interest in what went on around him, but he never said anything. So little did he say that Dotty and Nige thought he could not talk. They were wrong. He could, but he didn't care to. He just sat there most of the time, noticing things. He hadn't talked for so long that he sometimes wondered if he still could if he wanted to, but since he never wanted to, he quite reasonably concluded that it mattered little whether he could or couldn't. Anyway, whoever heard of a talking owl?

It was a rainy morning, two or three days after the barbecue, and the owl noticed various comings and goings – fairies and slugs arriving and leaving the Tree House which was now the new slug army barracks and headquarters. The other thing that the owl noticed was Elsie leaving the helicopter loft, at the controls of the remaining helicopter. Sitting next to her in the co-pilot seat was Ergo, and they were off to meet Horace the piano elf at the Don't Be So Ridiculous Valley Academy Of Music, to which establishment Horace had returned after the excitement of his adventure at Pigfrog Command. The piano was of course lost, left behind at Pigfrog HQ, but Ergo hoped one day to get it back. In the meantime, the elf had another one (which he had played on the night of the barbecue), but it wasn't his favourite instrument, and he often felt sad as he imagined big, slimy Ursula Moundrot plonking away at it with her ugly fat fingers.

By now, Ergo was on his fifth lesson, and had learned how to play two-note chords by stretching his knobbly bits wider and squeezing them into smaller points than were normally needed for other jobs. He had a good ear, and could pick out tunes with his right knobbly bits while accompanying himself with his left knobbly bits. His teacher was dead pleased.

"I've never seen anything like it," said Horace, and he hadn't.

Ergo was a natural. Five Woodland shillings was all it had cost to convert a non-musical slug into, well, a slightly less non-musical slug. And soon, because of this, Horace would be known throughout Don't Be So Ridiculous Valley and beyond, as a famous piano teacher. Not only that, but it had been Horace the piano elf who had saved everyone by tricking Ursula into playing a Morse code message when they were imprisoned at Pigfrog Command.

And so life went on in Don't Be So Ridiculous Valley and the little real valley near it, where the tree headquarters stood. Ergo spent a lot of time thinking about what to do next; how to retrieve the helicopter from Pigfrog Command, and how, eventually, to defeat the pigfrogs and their nasty old General. It wasn't going to be easy.

Meanwhile, Quirkhardt spied. He spied while he took Ergo his morning mug of pigeon's milk. He spied while he scrubbed floors and he spied while he pruned the plum tree that grew next to Dotty and Nige's Tree house, the headquarters of Slug Intelligence. He spied as he was led back each evening, by Arthur Monkberry, to his cell in the jail block which they had specially made for him. He schemed about how, one day, after plucking up enough courage to kill Elsie (which, he had decided, he would do with his eyes closed, as he couldn't bear the sight of blood), he would escape, with all his secret information, back to Pigfrog Command, and to the congratulations of his feared superior, General James Moundrot, D.S.O., B.C.C.C., C.P. (Dead Slug Order, Bronze Cha Cha Cha and Cycling Proficiency).

One night, a fearsome storm howled and raged outside as the slugs, trolls, gnome-adds, squirreloids and others huddled in their barrack rooms and tried unsuccessfully not to be afraid. Upstairs, Dotty and Nige huddled together in the big bed which they had bought one weekend from Woodland Beds For One And All, using some of the money they had made from Nigel's inventions. The lightning flashed at their window and the thunder growled and groaned until it surged up into big, sharp bangs which seemed to be right overhead.

In the middle of all this thunder and lightning, Malcolm One buzzed. Not just the sound – he actually felt buzzy. Malcolms Two and Three were loading up the Time Thimble with chocolate biscuits and ginger beer ready for their next adventure – a trip into the future; a Fact-Finding Mission, no less, into the dark and scary Unknown. Malcolm One was calm and serious on the outside, but as excited as, well, anything , on the inside. It didn't matter that it was a stormy night – the Time Thimble was never affected by the weather, because it would soon be flashing through tomorrow, the next day and the day after that, until it would all get faster and faster and spin around and around so that all the colours of the trees and the sky and the houses would mix up in a swishy sort of mush in front of their eyes. No wonder Malcolm felt buzzy inside.

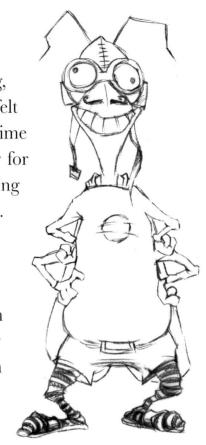

"I hope you'll come back," said Ergo, rather unnecessarily.

"So do we!" chorused the Time Flies. A great big clap of thunder boomed, just at the right time to add a dramatic touch to the blast-off.

"Thanks for staying up late to see us off!" shouted Malcolm Two, as the three waved, yelled and buzzed all at the same time.

With that, they were gone.

"My pleasure..." began Ergo, until he realised that his three newish friends had vanished – thimble, chocolate biscuits, ginger beer and all. He sighed, turned, and slowly made his way back to bed, where he fell asleep and dreamed once more of Little Else.

＊

That stormy night, General Moundrot cursed as he stood, heavy and damp, leaning against the rock face at the bottom of the central shaft of Pigfrog Command. Two junior officers from Second Battalion slouched nervously around as a pigfrog mechanic called Rigstay laboured under Dotty's helicopter, trying to work out how to get it going.

"I'm terribly sorry, your Generalness, but I'm going to need another week on this," the mechanic apologised. "I can't seem to discover what fuel they are using. It is obviously something powerful, but, funnily enough, it smells almost like... er, tea."

"Tea!" Moundrot exploded. "What sort of blithering clot are you? Why would they use tea?"

"With respect, Your Honour, I just said it smelled like tea, not actually *was* tea."

"Don't tell me what you meant," snapped Moundrot. "I know what you meant and you meant it was tea. I would demote you to the lowest of the low if you weren't already the lowest of the low. In fact, I might even create a new rank, even lower than that, just for you, you nasty, unpleasant little wart. Anybody knows you can't fly a helicopter on tea."

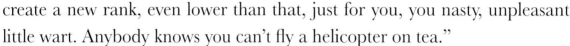

General Moundrot felt better now. He hadn't yelled at anyone all day and he had been beginning to have withdrawal symptoms. Headaches, dizziness – that sort of thing. But however much he was yelled at, Rigstay knew that as he was the only mechanic in Pigfrog Command, the General would not do anything really horrid to him. He needed him too much. Even so, Rigstay had a suspicion that perhaps it actually was tea. Not that he could say so now – now that the general had pronounced it not to be tea. If he proved it actually was tea, it would be like saying that the General was wrong, and Rigstay was cleverer than that. Not a lot cleverer, but a bit cleverer.

"I'll give you one more day, and then..." Moundrot began.

And then you'll do exactly what? thought the mechanic, but didn't say it.

Moundrot didn't finish the sentence, because he really couldn't think what he would do if his only mechanic failed to get the machine going. He turned on his heel and lurched out through the shaft entrance, followed by the two other officers. Rigstay saluted to their departing backs. Not the proper salute.

While Ergo slept, Quirkhardt was digging. He had been digging every night for two weeks now, and had nearly dug right under the wall of his cell. During the days, he had worked hard and spied harder. This had not left much time for sleep, and Quirkhardt was tired. But still he dug. As he dug, he thought about the very special secret he had learned from listening at the keyhole of Nigel Farnsbarnes' workshop. The information would certainly put him right back in Moundrot's good books, and his place on Ursula's sherry party list was in the bag. When he arrived back at Pigfrog Command to tell his secret to Moundrot, Moundrot would kiss him and hug him, he knew. Well, perhaps not, but he would be pleased when Quirkhardt told him that the captured helicopter would fly if only they would fill the tank with tea! With two sugars to the Woodland litre. This would be the secret information that would prove Quirkhardt's loyalty and earn him Moundrot's forgiveness for leading Third Battalion to its doom and tying up Mrs Moundrot. He shuddered. Had he really done that? He admired his own guts, just a little. What had he said to Moundrot through the door? He couldn't quite remember, but he knew it contained the words "fat", "slimy" and "scumbag". Would Moundrot really forgive him?

He had supplied Major Accuppa with a few little bits of information at a meeting in the bushes, one week after the garden party when Major Accuppa had first given him the chance to save himself, but this was different. He would break out of his cell this very night, kill Elsie and make his way back up to Pigfrog Command to give old Moundrot the news!

Quirkhardt carried on digging, deep into the stormy night.

In the morning Ergo awoke, determined. The storm had worked itself down into a pleasant drizzle that made the grass look greener than usual, and Ergo had a feeling that the air wasn't so heavy any more. He had decided that he would take Sodge and Arthur Monkberry up to Pigfrog Command, sneak past the sentries, get round to the top of the mountain and lower himself down into the main shaft (not to be confused with Moundrot's bedroom ventilation shaft!) and get the helicopter. He would then fly it back up the shaft... hang on a minute! He couldn't fly the helicopter, he was only a slug. So who could he take to fly it? Dotty? Nigel? or... Elsie! But he didn't really want to put the girl fairies in even more danger, and Nigel wasn't really the type for commando-style operations. Maybe Ergo *could* ask Elsie, after all. She had shown her tough qualities in the previous action, and was good at piloting the helicopter.

He hurried (as much as it is worth hurrying for a slug) down to Elsie's little room, where she always slept in the other little wooden bed bought by Nigel and Dotty at Woodland Beds For One And All, and where the cute little red curtains with strawberry patterns hung at the windows. It was sensible to hang them there, he thought, they would have looked stupid above the fire place, for example, and anyway curtains and windows were sort of meant for one another – just like himself and Elsie. He knocked on her little door. No answer. Perhaps she was asleep. He knocked a little louder. Then a little louder.

"Elsie?"

He rattled the handle.

"Elsie!"

There was no reply.

He pushed the door and it opened. Elsie was gone.

They looked everywhere for her, to no avail. Ergo got very worried.

"She wouldn't just leave. She must be somewhere."

It was when Arthur Monkberry discovered that Quirkhardt was missing that Ergo realised that things must be bad. He couldn't believe that even Quirkhardt would hurt Elsie. Surely nobody would do such a thing! But there she was, as clear as daylight – gone. Ergo decided to organise two search parties, one to go North East, towards Pigfrog Command, and the other to go South West, across the edge of Don't Be So Ridiculous Valley. They would both be called Search Party Number One – a tactic which had worked with the Carol Singing Squads. In Ergo's own party would be Monkberry, Sodge and Nigel, who had volunteered. Another thing Nigel had done, so that squirreloids were not required to breathe food-fuel into the windsocks of the slug wheels any more, was to invent the internal combustion engine.

"That's nice," Ergo had said.

The other search party would comprise Dotty, in the remaining helicopter, plus Horace the piano elf, with another troll called Stanley Spick, from Monkberry's Avocado Farmers, who was a dab hand at radio operating. This team would wait one day, and if Ergo did not return would set out to the South West. In the meantime, Dotty would circle the area in her helicopter, which, incidentally, was blue because it was a Wednesday morning.

Ergo couldn't believe all this was happening. He was becoming very distressed to think of Elsie lost, or worse. Why would she leave in the middle of the night with Quirkhardt? With extra provisions for three days and a large flask of tea he set off miserably with his chosen team of searchers, up the trail that led towards pigfrog country.

꙳

Even though Moundrot had everything a pigfrog could want – power, a lovely wife – well perhaps not exactly lovely, but a nice person – and a big box of chocolate cigars, he was far from happy that afternoon. He was lounging in his bedroom pothole, looking out of the small window slit and feeling impatient about Rigstay's progress with the flying machine when he felt that his patience was about to run out. In fact, he set his watch to 3.33pm as the time he expected it to happen. Sure enough, exactly at that time, it did. He was always right! This was not the way to crush the slug army, hanging about waiting for some idiot to mend a blithering flying machine. This wasn't how he got where he was today. He wanted to get out there and squash a few of the little buggers. Yes, squash a few. Squash...a...few. He liked to say it over and over in his mind, enjoying each imagined squash. Squelch, squash, squish, went the sound effect in his imagination. Lovely.

"Right! Forget all this boring mechanical nonsense!" shouted Moundrot to Major Accuppa, who had been topping up the chocolate cigar box for his boss. "Summon the officers in charge of First and Second Battalions! We are leaving to find their nasty little headquarters and jump on it, all at once, from a very great height! And then we'll move onwards and destroy their stupid little High Street town bit with the silly towers and houses, and squash everything that lives there!"

"But what about Quirkhardt, Sir? He's there, amongst them..." Accuppa reasoned.

"Yes, good, good, good!" dribbled Moundrot, embarking on an upwards spiral of spit-creating frenzy. "We'll descend upon them all – that's what we will do, DESCEND!"

Accuppa wasn't too enthusiastic about all this squashing stuff. It had been his very reluctance to jump on things fleshy that had led to his applying for the Catering Corps in the first place. Now his boss was going to take the entire Headquarters Division of the pigfrog army (since there were only two remaining battalions at Headquarters) and go slug-squashing – and that included Accuppa. But he would obey, and would alert the cream of the pigfrog officers' mess to the fact that they were to leave imminently for Woodland Land, where he himself had first located the Slug base. Something else – something rather timely – had just occurred to Accuppa. Maybe this is what had sub-consciously made his boss take immediate action. It was December the twenty-third, and snow had begun to fall. The real Christmas was about to happen, and Moundrot was obviously not planning to let it pass in an unpigfrog-like way.

⁓ⁱⁱ⁓

Two feet trudged up the mountain road with many miles to go before Pigfrog Command would loom up ahead. The owner of the feet was a bedraggled, exhausted but optimistic Quirkhardt, carrying over his shoulder the small but very much alive bundle of Little Else, bound hand and foot. The night before he had crept into Elsie's room with a sharp dagger, determined to carry out the grizzly task, but to his own disgust had not been able to bring himself to perform the deed. Elsie had awoken with a start, and Quirkhardt had collapsed in tears at the end of her bed and blurted out the whole story. She had been compassionate, listening to his tale with mounting horror and sympathy. He had explained that, even though he couldn't bring himself to kill her, neither could he let her go – his chivalry did not extend so far as to risk his own life when Moundrot realised what Quirkhardt had – or hadn't – done. At least if he could deliver Elsie to Moundrot, perhaps he and she could work out a way of her escaping afterwards, so that it didn't look like

Quirkhardt's fault. Since he had spared her life, and more importantly, since Quirkhardt was bigger than her and had a dagger, Elsie agreed. So that is how Quirkhardt came to be trudging towards Pigfrog Command on the next day, as the snow began falling, with Elsie over his shoulder.

"Would you like to rest for a while?" asked Quirkhardt to the bundle on his shoulder.

"Well, the blood is rather going to my head, Mr Quirkhardt," said Elsie, trying to be just a tiny bit jolly. She actually felt horrible, and frightened, but didn't want Quirkhardt to know.

"Alright, then, we'll stop," wheezed her captor as he flopped her down on the stumpy grass at the side of the trail. He had really wanted the rest for himself, and yet he couldn't help feeling a little sorry for Elsie. He pulled out a piece of banana cake that he had saved from his dinner the night before, broke it in two and gave the slightly smaller half to her. He stretched out on the grass and looked at the sky, confident that she could not escape, being bound hand and foot. He was feeling weary, and far from confident about what Moundrot would do. The old grouch was known for being deceitful and sly. That's what made him such a successful pigfrog. Quirkhardt wanted to win his approval but wasn't sure that he wanted to see the slugs crushed by Moundrot. But, if it was himself or the slugs dying, there was no contest as to which he preferred. As he thought these things, he looked over at Elsie and noticed a tear in one of her eyes. He turned away quickly so that she would not be aware that he had been looking at her.

As he looked away, he saw something that nearly brought tears to his own eyes. Far away, up the gradual slope at the foot of the mountain range ahead of him, about a mile away, he could see, and now he could hear, the entire pigfrog army – Headquarters Division, Battalions One and Two – and out in front, even at this distance, he could clearly make out the shape, and somehow feel the heavy presence of General James Moundrot, D.S.O., B.C.C.C., C.P.

Quirkhardt's heart began to beat faster.

"Treble Blithering Goo-Gobs!" he muttered.

"And the rest!" added Little Else.

Next Chapter: Looking For Little Else

Ergo's wheels were now faster than ever, thanks to Nigel Farnsbarnes' internal combustion thingy. He and Sodge could go quite quickly over the rough ground, and even Arthur Monkberry had to trot alongside to keep up. But the search was not proving fruitful. Elsie was nowhere to be seen.

"What an appalling situation," offered Monkberry in his Prince Charles voice.

"I'm not giving up, Arthur," said Ergo, defiantly. "She could always be just around the next corner." As they turned the next corner, and Elsie wasn't there, Ergo looked at Sodge and Arthur as if to say "But then again..."

It began to snow – just light, wet snow that didn't settle on the ground. Ergo and the others had forgotten that it was nearly Christmas because their thoughts were with Little Else, wherever she was. They continued up the trail, higher up into the foothills of Everywhere Else. Arthur tried to raise their spirits with some folk and farming songs from the Avocado Basin, but as they had titles like "Death And Disease To Him Who Raids My Trees" they didn't raise Ergo's spirits very much.

⁓⁓⁓

If there had been music accompanying Moundrot's advance down towards the Slug headquarters, it would have been loud kettle drums and dark, low trombone notes. He had death on his mind as he stomped along at the head of his army, and he dribbled at the thought of all the thousands of slugs who would soon be reduced to slug pâté under his weight and that of his troops. He grunted with satisfaction as he dragged his trail of goo down the

122

wide mountain trail, and he silently wished himself a Merry Christmas. As the army reached a plateau on a cliff face half way down the mountain, and on a gradual bend to the left, Moundrot had a good view of the ground ahead of him for about a mile or so. There was something out there. A figure of somebody perhaps carrying firewood or something. Moundrot stopped and his army shuffled to a shambolic halt behind him. He raised his field glasses and peered through them. Magnified by the strong lenses, he could clearly see a pigfrog pushing his way through a light snowfall, carrying a bundle on his back. Quirkhardt! Moundrot's heart skipped a beat. So Quirkhardt had fallen for it! This was going to be good! He was probably on his way back to plead for mercy – and with any luck, spill the beans about all sorts of slug secrets. Moundrot would listen, pretend to forgive, and then when it was all over – when the slugs were defeated and everybody was back at Pigfrog Command – he would gleefully mince Quirkhardt from the feet up, even more slowly than he had previously threatened!

The distant Quirkhardt got less and less distant; nearer and nearer, bigger and bigger. Moundrot waited. He fixed his face into his best fatherly smile, and waited. It wasn't long before Quirkhardt had arrived, quivering with fear and dread, at the feet of his commander.

"Quirkhardt, my dear fellow, how... er... nice to see you," said Moundrot. If Quirkhardt had been even five percent less terrified and about eight percent more intelligent he might have realised that this could not possibly have been the real Moundrot speaking, and he might have smelled a rat. But the rat went unsmelled. Quirkhardt was so relieved not to be shouted at or killed that he dropped Elsie in an undignified heap on the floor and fell to his knees.

"General, how can you forgive me?" he grovelled. "But I only escaped from the jail with that slug because I was sure he was up to no good and I wanted to find out more about his plans, and I had to shout those rude words through the door at you to make him think I was really on his side, and I don't really think you are a fat scumbag, er, well, what I mean is, not any sort of scumbag at all, fat, thin, or... well, anyway, and so I escaped, and by the way, thanks for making me a Lance Corporal, I really appreciate that, and... oh... yes, I've got some information for you, as well as... I've got the nasty little slug chief's... er, girlfriend here, all tied up and everything... Sir."

He then pulled out a box of chocolate cigars he had bought for this very purpose at the Woodland Candy Shop on the morning of his escape, and handed it triumphantly to the general. That ought to do it, thought Quirkhardt.

"Hmmm... well, jolly good," began Moundrot, who of course didn't believe a word of it, but wanted to relish and prolong Quirkhardt's plight. "I now promote you to the rank of Major. Well, done!"

Quirkhardt's fear sipped away and was replaced by a warm glow of delight, pride and relief.

"And the information you have for me?" asked Moundrot, sweetly.

"Oh, yes, Sir. I have managed, at great personal risk and with utmost use of my Officer Material qualities, to discover that the slug army helicopter is powered, believe it or not, by tea! Normal, ordinary tea, with two sugars to the Woodland litre!"

Moundrot's face went a sort of grey colour. His cheeks puffed out and his eyes looked as if they were about to pop out. But he restrained himself from knocking Quirkhardt off the nearby cliff face, because he wanted to keep him alive for longer – sudden death would have been too kind. He composed himself, and resumed his sweet smile.

"How... er, interesting, Major. Thank you. Thank you so much."

At least now he could get the helicopter going one day, even if he looked an idiot in Gritwart's eyes; but Gritwart's opinion of him did not figure in Moundrot's concerns.

"Now about this – er, fairy person. I think we should push her off the cliff. I'll let you do it, because you deserve it after all you've been through."

Quirkhardt swallowed hard. He didn't want Elsie to die, but he liked being a major, and this was the very first time Moundrot had ever been nice to him. What a dilemma. Well, actually no dilemma at all, but a pity that she should have to die.

"Ooh, thanks, Sir!" he exclaimed, with fake enthusiasm. He lifted Elsie to her feet. Her arms were tied behind her. She had that look on her face that people have when they are about to be thrown off cliffs. Quirkhardt, watched by the entire pigfrog army, led her to the edge of the cliff, but as they reached the edge, he leaned over, unseen by Moundrot, and loosened the knot tying her arms.

"Goodbye forever you nasty horrible little fairy effort!" he shouted, giving her a shove, and a great cheer went up through the pigfrog ranks. Elsie plummeted downwards and out of sight. Moundrot took out two chocolate cigars, put one in his mouth and offered the other to Quirkhardt.

Elsie plunged down and down, struggling with the rope around her. If you have to be thrown off a cliff, it's best to be thrown off a very high one, philosophised Elsie, as she tried desperately to get free of her bonds before hitting the hard ground at the bottom of the cliff. She couldn't work out whether it was her life flashing before her, or a load of old rocks, but something was making her feel decidedly dizzy; possibly the thought of imminent death. She knew if she could just free herself she could use her wings to save her. It seemed like about three Woodland minutes, but was actually only twenty-five Woodland seconds before she looked down to see the ground almost dead ahead of her, and rising quickly towards her, as it seemed. Just at this moment, she broke out of her bonds, her wings popped out and she was suddenly able once again to fly – upwards and sideways out of view of the pigfrogs, and to safety! Being a fairy had its advantages, as she had discovered before.

Stupid old General Moundrot wouldn't have thought of it, but Quirkhardt had. He was a cowardly, selfish pigfrog, but he had a heart somewhere underneath all that nastiness. Quite a long way under it, as it happened, but somewhere deep down in there. Deep, deep down.

Moundrot marched on. His army dutifully followed. This was going to be his moment of glory. The destruction of Slug HQ and all who lived there. Lovely, lovely, lovely! It would only be another six hours or so before they would arrive at Woodland Land, whereupon they would do a lot of jumping upon a lot of slugs, fairies, squirreloids and trolls. The Christmas spirit wasn't dead. Life wasn't too bad after all, really.

❧

Ergo was frantic. He radioed back to HQ, where Dotty and the others had

125

Arriving at Pigfrog Command to look for Little Else

now returned after their fruitless search to the South West.

"We are heading towards Pigfrog Command, following the old Woodland Railway line and then skirting around the back of the mountain to observe Pigfrog Command from behind," he told Dotty. This was because he didn't want to be spotted by any pigfrog scouts as he approached. He was also worried in case there might be pigfrog girl guides, cubs or brownies around, to watch his approach and alert Moundrot. Ergo had no idea that the pigfrog army had been mobilised – and his chosen route meant, quite accidentally, that he and his party did not run into them or them into him. As Moundrot and his forces were heading down the front of the mountain, Ergo, Sodge, Arthur Monkberry and Nigel Farnsbarnes were making their way up the back of it. Monkberry had thoughtfully brought along a large bag of mint humbugs and all four were sucking away happily. The sucking was in fact the only happy thing about them, as they plodded sadly up the snowy hill, pushing against the prevailing wind.

While he trudged and sucked, Ergo reflected on the fact that it is actually possible for your mouth to be happy and your feet to be sad, both at the same time. It also struck him that a prevailing wind was the only wind one could ever push against, since if a wind wasn't prevailing it wasn't blowing, and so you could hardly push against it, could you? These thoughts occupied his mind for a short time, but he was mostly thinking about Little Else. Where was she? What had Quirkhardt done to her? How could he manage without her? She, with her lovely tweed two-piece and cute smile, kept popping into his thoughts and he began to lose interest in his mint humbug, which was nearly finished anyway.

As they reached the top of the back of the mountain – where Ergo had once emerged from Moundrot's ventilation shaft – all four of them dropped down into a lying position, except Ergo and Sodge who were already lying down, what with being slugs and everything.

"The bigger shaft comes out over here," pointed out Monkberry, from his lying down position. "That's the one where the light shines down in front of the prison cells. If Quirkhardt has brought her back, that's where she'll be."

The four of them crawled towards the large shaft and peered carefully over the top and down into the shaft, or crater. It was quite wide, being the central area around which Pigfrog Command was built, and was a little like the hole that goes down through the middle of a volcano, with windows cut into it all the way down. By now, Ergo knew that Moundrot's accommodation was fairly high up in the shaft, and the other accommodation was situated below it, down and down until the prison cells would be quite a long way below. At the bottom of the shaft it was quite dark. The place seemed strangely empty. There was definitely some activity, some sounds coming from the various pigfrog rooms, but nowhere near the amount of activity he would have expected. Peering deep into the cavity, he could just make out a light shining. It was just enough light to allow him to see, after squinting for some time down the shaft, that there were two pigfrog legs sticking out from underneath something... and that the something from under which the legs were sticking out was... the helicopter! Rigstay was lying underneath Nigel's flying machine, tinkering with it while the rest of the army was at that very moment marching towards Slug HQ.

Ergo immediately decided to try to rescue the helicopter. He knew that Elsie was a priority, but this was too good an opportunity to miss, and it might even lead to finding Elsie, particularly if she was back in the pigfrog jail. Monkberry would secure ropes which would lower them all over the edge. Once they were at the bottom, they would creep up, empty Ergo's thermos flask of tea into the fuel tank, and then Arthur would take the controls while they would take off, leaving the pigfrog mechanic lying there tinkering with a helicopter that suddenly wouldn't be there any more. Monkberry pulled ropes from his backpack and started to secure them to a tree stump, which had it not been there, would have spoiled everything.

As they all peered over the edge of the crater, something not too clever happened. Nigel's mint humbug fell out of his mouth, and to his horror fell down, down, downwards until, far below, they heard it bounce off one Rigstay's legs and into his open toolbox.

"Nigel, for such a genius you really are a flipping idiot!" scolded Ergo, as they heard the sound of the mint humbug landing just where they didn't need it to.

Rigstay jumped up and looked around. Finding

the humbug in his toolbox, he did two things. Firstly, he popped it into his mouth so as not to waste it, and secondly he looked up the shaft to see where it had come from. He remembered the time when it had rained jelly babies, and this didn't seem much sillier. In fact, it was slightly less silly. Let's say that the jelly babies raining would be, on a silliness scale of one to ten, about nine, then a mint humbug dropping out of the sky would be about a six. However, just as a precaution, Rigstay looked up the shaft. He couldn't really see what was happening up there but he knew something was wrong. He reach out and pressed a small purple button at the doorway of the workshop area, and a loud alarm bell began to ring.

"That's torn it!" yelled Ergo. But instead of hurrying away from the area, Ergo's leadership qualities and bravery took over, and he shouted instructions to the others to hurry up and lower themselves down the shaft even more quickly.

"Maybe we can take them by surprise," he said.

"But they've been warned already," protested Sodge.

"Exactly! So they'll hardly be expecting anyone to come dangling down on a bit of rope while the alarm is ringing. People don't do that sort of thing."

"I wonder why?" muttered Nigel as he obediently slipped over the edge with Ergo, Sodge and Monkberry and descended into the crater and towards the ringing bell.

_~\|/~_

After ringing the alarm bell Rigstay waited for the guards to arrive, and sucked on his mint humbug, which had formerly been Nigel's. He thought it was strange that it was taking a long time for anyone to react to the alarm, and then of course he realised that most of the army was out squashing slugs. This left a few domestic pigfrog attendants, gardeners, females and youngsters, all of whom would expect somebody other than themselves to react to an alarm. There were one or two main door guards on duty, but they would not be allowed to leave their posts. Usually there would have been plenty of other soldiers around to attend to an alarm.

"Anyway," thought Rigstay, "nothing's happened. I'll switch the alarm off." Looking up to check that all was fine up through the crater, he was surprised to see a very close-up view of Arthur Monkberry's boots descending rapidly down a rope into his face.

"Ouuffh!" exclaimed Rigstay, as he fell to the floor and went into a deep dream, in which General Moundrot and he were having tea together, and young lady ballerina pigfrogs danced around them in a cloud of soft, blue smoke.

"Right! Get that mechanic chappie out of the way, Arthur!" ordered Ergo, unstrapping the flask of tea and moving round to the back of the helicopter to find the fuel tank.

"Nige, you jump in and start her up, please, Mate!" said Ergo to Nigel.

He said "please" to Nigel because, to Ergo, Nigel was more of a civilian than a troop.

"Aye, Aye! O Great Sluggy Leader!" answered Nigel, suddenly feeling more like a troop than a civilian. He was wishing his dear, sweet wife, Dotty, could see him being such a hero – absailing into the enemy headquarters and piloting the lost helicopter home. He kicked the starter and revved on the throttle. It coughed into action and the rotor blades began to turn. Yes!

"Jump in, then!" he called to Ergo, Sodge and Monkberry, who were already doing so.

The little pink helicopter (for it was a Thursday afternoon) rose slowly up through the crater and past each window of pigfrog command. If anybody was there, they must have just thought that Gritwart had got the thing going at last. Some domestic pigfrogs even looked out and waved as they went past.

As they drew level with the jail windows, Monkberry beamed his very strong troll standard issue torch into the cells which circled the crater at that height. There was no-one there. No Elsie. No-one.

"I didn't dare hope she'd really be here," said Ergo, sadly, "but we'll keep looking for Quirkhardt on the way back – I'm sure we'll find them."

Just as the helicopter was level with the top windows inside the crater, and just as Nigel was about to throttle up and away, Ergo shouted, "What's that sound?"

"The rotor blades, of course!" answered technically-minded Nigel.

"No, no, listen!" urged Ergo. "It sounds like music... piano music." And of course, sure enough it was. Well, it was the sound of a piano anyway. Whether it was music was really a matter for each individual listener to decide. To Ursula Moundrot's ears it was music, for it was once again she who was playing. Ergo had heard the distant strains of the instrument as they had hovered up past Ursula's window. Looking in, he could now see her looking out at him and the others in the helicopter with an expression of horror on her ugly, greeny-pink face.

Ergo looked over to Monkberry with one of those "are you thinking what I'm thinking?" looks.

"Let's rescue the piano!" shouted Ergo. Nige steadied the helicopter and Sodge acted as winch man, fixing and holding the ropes while Monkberry and Ergo swung into the open window and landed on the floor right in front of the terrified Ursula Moundrot.

"Stand aside, Mrs M!" was all Ergo could think of, but it seemed appropriate. Ursula scuttled out of the way while Monkberry grabbed the piano in his long, muscular troll-type arms. Ergo steadied it and tied the ropes around it. Jumping onto the top of the piano, Monkberry and Ergo gave the signal and the helicopter rose slowly and the piano swung out of the window, dangling like... well, like a piano dangling from a helicopter – with Monkberry and Ergo sitting on it.

Then, to their utmost surprise – and shock – Ursula called out of the window.

"I'm coming too! Don't leave me behind!" with which she launched her fat body off the window sill into mid-air, landing on the top of the piano next to Monkberry, for whom there was already little enough room.

"What?" shouted Monkberry.

"Don't leave me here. Let me come too. Please, please, ever so pretty, pretty please!"

Ergo couldn't work it out. Was it that she couldn't bear to be parted from the piano, or was it that she wanted to get away from Moundrot and start a new life, or something? Anyway, he didn't have time to spend thinking about it. By now he had climbed almost into the helicopter and was waiting for Monkberry to join him, leaving the piano dangling.

"There isn't room!" he shouted down to Ursula. But she looked so frantic

and pathetic and... vulnerable... that he took pity on her.

"Well, just this once!" he relented – as if there would ever be another time!

"Oh, thank you, thank you, and double..."

"Just get in!" yelled Monkberry, giving her a hefty shove so that she landed with a thud, face down in the back of the flying machine, with her large scaly pigfrog legs sticking out through the open window hatch. Moundrot hauled himself up and into the helicopter after her. Nigel pulled back on something, stepped on something, and switched something else, and the helicopter was up and out of the crater, with all five occupants struggling hard not to fall out, and the piano swinging underneath.

"Good job I brought that flask of tea!" said Ergo.

The Pigfrogs Are Coming

It was the afternoon of Christmas Eve, and Dotty, having returned fruitlessly from her search to the South West, was sitting miserably watching the snow falling across the flat, scrubby ground that led off in the direction of the hill that was Don't Be So Ridiculous Valley. It had been a third of a kettle boil since dear Nigel and lovely Ergo had left, and Dotty was dying for a cup of tea. She worried desperately about her poor sister, Little Elsie, and all the other things that she was obviously worried about.

She decided to go down to the barrack room where there was a proper kettle so that she could have a proper cup of tea and relax while she worried. As she arrived at the barrack room, where many of the slugs and gnome-adds slept, she came across Sir John Marvellousbloke, the name-giver, who was peering through a telescope and humming an old slug sea shanty.

"Afternoon, Sir John," she said. She had always thought it a bit unfair for him to have chosen "Sir" for his first name and "John" for his second name. It made him seem more important than all the others. Fairies never had that problem – their mummies and daddies chose their names and that was that. But as the official slug name-giver, he had rather taken advantage of the situation. The irony was, however, that he actually was a marvellous bloke. Perhaps if you named yourself that, you would just become one as a matter of obligation. She wondered if, had he called himself, say, "Sir John Nastyperson", that maybe he would have become one of those instead.

"Afternoon, Dotty," he answered, cheerily. He doubled as a lookout when he wasn't being a name-giver. "Just checking the horizon for, you know, anything..."

The wooden floor was cold, and Dotty went straight over to the kettle and flicked it on.

"Cup of tea?" she asked Sir John.

"What an utterly delightful idea," he responded, in his marvellous bloke voice. He peeped once more through his telescope. He peeped again. "Dotty, I think there's something out there."

"What, let me see!" Dotty's tone brightened.

Peering through the telescope, Dotty could see a small thing, flying through the blizzard. She waited as it got nearer and then... yes, she could now clearly see that it was dear Little Else, flying along, battling against the snowy weather.

"It's Little Else!" shouted Dot, jumping up, grabbing Sir John and dancing him around the room. The cup of tea was forgotten. Sir John rushed off to tell the others, most of whom were in the barrack dining hall next door, roasting chestnuts. Dotty ran back up to the balcony where she told the Large Disused Owl, and they both waved at the ever-clearer figure of Little Else as she approached. When she landed, exhausted on the balcony, Dotty hugged her and took her inside.

"You're back!" she cried.

"I know," said Elsie.

"Well, what happened?"

"Oh, goodness, Dot, it's such a long story. But the most important thing is that there is a huge pigfrog army marching on us now, and it's only about one Woodland hour away from us. They plan to jump – collectively, so to speak – on us from a great height, and thus turn us all from lumpy to flat."

"Oh, blither!" said Dotty.

"Quite. But we have to do something, and fast. Where is Ergo?"

"He went searching for you with Nigel, Arthur and Sodge, but we haven't heard from them for ages. I think they might have radio problems."

"Triple and quintuple blither!" said Elsie. "Well, we have to do something."

Just then, Sir John came rushing up into the tree house, where the two fairy sisters were.

"There's a..." he began.

"...huge army of pigfrogs approaching from the direction of Everywhere Else?" Dotty completed the sentence.

"How did you ...? Oh, never mind. But we'll have to do something," said Sir John.

"We were just saying that," said Dotty.

᠁

Meanwhile, Ergo and the others were flying as fast as they could, back to base, oblivious to the dangers that their loved ones faced, and unaware of the fact that, for the moment at least, Elsie was safe. They flew over the mountains of Everywhere Else and followed the Unbelievably Smelly River back to the Avocado Basin, and towards the bit near Don't Be So Ridiculous Valley, with the piano swinging underneath the helicopter; but they were at least two Woodland hours away, and were doubtful whether Ergo's flask of tea would be enough fuel to get them all the way home.

᠁

The pigfrog army got nearer and nearer. Froon, who was conferring with the other military leaders of the slug army, decided to evacuate the barracks. They would retreat to the plains, or Flat Bits as they called them, to the South, and watch, and hope for something nice to happen, like the entire pigfrog army suddenly developing food poisoning and pneumonia all at the same time. The slugs were, however, still armed to the teeth, and had all their depth charges and other weapons, together with the trolls, their most valued fighters, who each carried a crossbow and a huge quiver of bolts. What they didn't have was their leader, their inspiration; their Ergo.

"What a way to spend Christmas!" complained Slarjk, the flower-cutter, as they all tramped miserably off into the snowy Flat Bits and dug in to keep themselves a little warmer. Dotty and Elsie took charge of the remaining helicopter and others helped to cover it in snow so that it wouldn't be noticed. They all waited and hoped.

Moundrot's advance scouts had told him to expect a small wooden peak at the top of a tree, and then a series of wooden buildings leading away from the tree house, and here it was, ahead of him, not very far away! Pigfrogs rarely ventured outside Everywhere Else, which is why slugs living at Don't Be So Ridiculous Valley had never had any trouble from them before. It had only been Ergo's passion to stop the injustice of their murderous activities and avenge Dotty's and Elsie's poor brother which had led to the present situation. Consequently, pigfrogs were not generally familiar with the whereabouts of the area of the tree house. Major Accuppa had been there – and Quirkhardt, of course, who was now at the old boy's side, leading him along and showing him the way.

The pigfrog army pounded its way relentlessly towards the little headquarters, and as it did so Moundrot got more and more excited at the idea of squashing everything in his sight. When they had reached a point very close to the Tree house and barracks he called forward his senior warrant officer, Sergeant Major Pockflab, and ordered him to halt the army and fan out in a formation which would surround the slug headquarters. This would be Moundrot's great moment; the moment when he would wipe out the entire enemy, together with all their friends and loved ones, all in one final, fatal strike.

Quietly and stealthily, the many hundreds of large, sweaty pigfrogs moved into position. With drooling lips, Moundrot waited until he felt the moment was right. Then, with one quick movement of the head, he nodded to the

Sergeant Major, and at the same time launched himself into the air, using his powerful, muscular hind legs. At that same moment, every pigfrog in First and Second Battalions did the same. They seemed to hang in the air for a brief moment, and then came whistling down, screaming the horrible pigfrog battle cry.

Moundrot, having been the first to launch, was the first to land and he went right through the roof of the Tree house, destroying in his wake the entire loft area and extension to the Disused Owl Hole – from which thankfully the Large Disused Owl had been evacuated. Quirkhardt had landed next to his General, and destroyed all of Dotty and Nigel's sitting room and the special chair lift that Ergo used to use to get up the stairs. All the other pigfrogs found similar targets, and the entire Slug Headquarters was destroyed in one moment – barracks, barrack dining hall, gardens and all – except the actual tree in which the tree house had originally been built before it had been extended.

There was silence. Only the soft sound of the wind could be heard, and through the mist and lightly falling powdered snow, the pigfrogs could see each other, standing silently in the pile of matchwood which was the ruins of Slug Headquarters, waiting for whatever would happen next. It was a grunt

from Moundrot that broke the silence. He presumed there would be slugs in the wreckage, but his toes and hind leg claws could not feel anything squishy. Hhm... maybe they had been completely squashed into the ground.

"Sergeant Major, get this wreckage pulled away. Clear the area," he barked.

The wreckage was pushed aside, and still Moundrot could see no slugs. The light was beginning to fade a little now, and a blue sheen began to appear on the soft snow around what was once Slug Headquarters. Moundrot began to grunt more. He was thinking very angry thoughts, and was beginning to think that he might have missed the best bit – that he might have been duped. If the slug army was not destroyed, where was it? Where were the little...? As he thought, his eye fell upon the glint of something, maybe a spear or crossbow arrowhead, or the tip of somebody's helmet in the snow, some distance off.

"Sshhh...!"

Moundrot wasn't stupid. He was everything else, but he wasn't stupid. He looked out into the dimming afternoon light, and he knew. He knew they were there, the little blighters! They were all out there, hiding in the snow. He turned slowly, caught the eye of his Sergeant Major, and then that of the next officer in line, which was the reluctant Major Accuppa. All three turned slowly and silently, and the word was whispered along the line. Soon the entire army was moving together towards the slugs, trolls, fairies, squirreloids and gnome-adds who waited fearfully and quietly.

Froon, Elsie and Dotty were with Stanley Spick, the troll radio operator, and had been trying to get Ergo on the radio, with no luck. The fact was, Ergo had left his radio at the edge of the crater of Pigfrog Command before he had lowered himself down with the others to rescue the helicopter.

"It's no good," whispered Spick, "they'll be no help. May I suggest we let the enemy have it – with everything we've got – before they get any closer?"

"It won't be enough. There are too many of them," said Froon. He was right. When the slugs had beaten the pigfrogs before, the pigfrogs had numbered only one battalion – now there were two at least, by Froon's estimation, and whereas before the pigfrogs had on that occasion been led by the idiotic Captain Quirkhardt, now they were led by their charismatic and feared General. The slug army, apart from not being up to full strength, lacked its own leader.

"Well, we'll do the best we can!" said Elsie.

"Froon, pass word to everyone to be ready to show themselves, on my signal."

"OK, Elsie, it's all we can do," Froon answered, bravely. He was surprised and pleased to see Elsie being so much in command. Somehow, some of Ergo's strength shone through Elsie now. It made him feel better. Just then, Little Elsie decided what to do. She stood up.

Moundrot was startled.

"You... You're supposed to be..."

"Dead?"

"We pushed you off a cliff!"

"Yes, and you've just jumped all over Slug Headquarters without inflicting a single casualty. Not very effective, are you, General?"

Moundrot wasn't used to being talked to like this. Steam seemed to be coming out from just behind his ears.

"You'll soon see how effective we are," he replied. He allowed himself a sideways sneer towards his Sergeant Major, hoping for a sneer back. A shared sneer is always so much nicer.

Elsie looked behind her and gestured to the others.

"We are going to drive you away and destroy your army, General. If you try to kill us we will just come right back again, as I have done this afternoon after you so unchivalrously pushed me off a cliff."

She was bluffing, because only fairies could fly, but she thought it might frighten Moundrot a little to think she was, somehow, invincible. At Elsie's signal, the slug army broke cover and showed itself behind her – slugs to the centre, gnome-adds and squirreloids to the left flank and trolls to the right. A look of bewilderment came over Moundrot's face. He hadn't expected opposition of this sort, and had by now lost the element of surprise. Still, he outnumbered the enemy many times, and his warriors were bigger than all but the trolls, who were about the same size as his own soldiers.

"We will crush you," said Moundrot.

He looked over to Sergeant Major Pockflab.

"Are you ready, Sarn't Major?"

"Yes, Sir," came the reply.

Moundrot sneered once more. This time it was a solo sneer.

The trolls raised their loaded crossbows. The slugs, on their new internal combustion-powered wheels, felt for their depth charges and other weapons. This was going to be some fight; but Elsie and Froon knew that against these odds, it was a battle they could never hope to win. Moundrot raised one green and scaly hand, ready to give the command. Elsie stood firm.

Just then, a grand piano fell out of the sky and knocked General Moundrot out. A great shout went up among the slug ranks, and they knew Ergo had arrived! Elsie looked up and saw the helicopter, bulging with people including Mrs Moundrot, and she breathed a sigh of something. Not of relief, yet, however. There was the small matter of two battalions of pigfrogs to deal with first.

Each pigfrog looked over at his fallen General, up at the troll bowmen, down at the slugs bristling with weapons – then turned and ran. All, that is, except Majors Quirkhardt and Accuppa, who threw up their arms and sank to their knees in surrender, and pleaded that they had not wanted to be a part of the whole thing in the first place.

Not knowing anything about what was going on, the arriving helicopter had flown around the back of what had once been Slug HQ and then, unable to land, had circled over the lined-up ranks of soldiers ready to do battle. Nobody on the battlefield had noticed the approaching flying machine, being so preoccupied with other business. As the helicopter had circled over Moundrot and Elsie, it had been Ursula Moundrot who had had the inspiration to lean forward and cut the rope holding the piano, using an army penknife which Jim had once given to her for Christmas. By now she had become tired of constantly being in fear of Moundrot, and wanted to escape the clutches of her despotic partner. It had been a risky and brave thing to do, but it had had the desired effect.

Euphoria broke out once again.

"That cat is always breaking out! We'll catch her later," said Nigel as Euphoria ran off after the fleeing pigfrogs. Elsie and Dotty went over to Ergo and Nigel and greeted them.

"Oh, beautiful brave, clever hubby-in-a-million!" yelled Dotty, reaching into the glove compartment of the helicopter and pulling out two raw onions (which were still there from before the capture of the aircraft, and still fairly clean).

She bowled one to him, and he caught it with one hand.

"What better time to share a raw onion than in a moment of victory!" she exclaimed.

"You're not wrong, there!" agreed Nigel, beaming with pride, and biting into his onion.

"It brings tears to your eyes, doesn't it?" Elsie said to Ergo as she hugged him and began to think about what fabric to have for her wedding dress.

"Merry Christmas – and then some!" shouted Ergo, to all his brave troops.

⁓⁓⁓

Three days later, Moundrot woke up with four headaches, which was one more than Ergo had received when he himself had been hit by the piano. But whereas Ergo had been wearing his helmet, Moundrot had no time for helmets – he thought they were for sissies – and had suffered much more serious injury. Moundrot started by opening one eye, just as he had done during the previous September Awakening. He rolled his eyeball around to see what was happening before he judged it to be safe to open the other one. When both eyes focussed, he could see that he was in a medical tent, and somebody – a nurse – was fussing about, preparing something. The nurse had her back to him, and she was bending over. This immediately enabled him to recognise her as – could it really be? – his dear wife, the lovely (well not really lovely, but a nice person) Ursula!

He looked down at his arms and realised that he was chained to the bed.

Funny. Ursula had never done that to him before. He tried to pull at them, but couldn't move.

Ursula had felt that she must look after him. The tent was part of a campsite which the slugs had constructed to keep everybody warm and safe until they were able to rebuild their home. She was frightened that he would be violent towards her, and was glad that Monkberry had thought to chain him to the bed.

"Hello, darling. How lovely to see you," he found himself saying. Ursula thought she hadn't quite heard properly.

"What did you say?" she asked.

"I said, how nice to see you, my dear. Is it Christmas yet? I'm sorry but I don't remember what happened or where we are."

Ursula wasn't used to hearing General Jim talk to her – or anybody – as politely as this.

"You have been unconscious for three days," Ursula informed him. "And do you know something, Jim? They've been the nicest three days of my life. The slugs defeated our army and you were knocked out by a piano falling from a helicopter onto your head."

She was expecting an angry reply, but felt she ought to be truthful from now on, and not hide her feelings.

"What, those nice little slugs? Why would they want to do a thing like that?" asked Moundrot. "I always thought they were such nice chaps, especially their leader, what's his name... Iago?"

"Ergo," Ursula corrected him. She was flabber-gasted. The knock on the head had had quite an effect on Moundrot. Could he have forgotten all that had happened on Christmas Eve?

"You attacked them and destroyed their home and tried to squash them all, with First and Second Battalions, on Christmas Eve," she told him, indignantly.

"Oh, did I? What a horrible thing! Most uncivil of me. I hope nobody was hurt. Can't imagine what must've come over me – it's quite out of character," said Moundrot.

Ursula couldn't believe what she was hearing.

"Wait there!" she said, rather unnecessarily, since he was chained to the bed. She ran over to Ergo's tent, where she found Ergo and Little Else, playing the card game 'Happy Families'.

"Have you got... Mr Bun, the Baker?" Ergo was saying to Else.

"Nope! Haha! Have you got Miss Rice, the grocer's daughter?" Elsie asked.

"Sorry to interrupt, General Ergo," began Ursula, "but could you please come quickly? It's my husband. He's woken up and seems to be talking complete nonsense."

Ergo and Elsie went straight over to the medical tent and followed Ursula in through the door flap.

"Darling, it's General Ergo and his fiancee, Little Elsie," Ursula said to Moundrot, rather as if it was hospital visiting time and Ergo and Elsie might have some flowers and grapes.

"Well, you old scoundrel, what have you got to say for yourself?" Ergo said, sternly.

"Ah, General... Ergo. And, er, Miss Elsie. It is so kind of you to visit me. But before anything else I do believe I have an apology to make," said Moundrot.

Ergo and Elsie looked at one another with that sort of raised-eyebrow-look that says "this ought to be interesting".

"My dear wife tells me that I acted in, shall we say, an... unneighbourly fashion, and I'd like you to know that it really isn't like me at all, and I'm terribly, terribly sorry. How can I make amends?"

Ergo thought it might be a trick. He told Moundrot in no uncertain terms that he had better jolly well mean it – and that if he was as changed as he claimed to be (not that he seemed to remember ever having been nasty in the first place) he could get the entire pigfrog army and tell them to rebuild the tree house and the barrack rooms and everything.

"And then, you had better sign a letter saying you will never try to squash anybody ever again," added Elsie, with a frown.

"Squash anybody? I would never dream of it! I would never think of doing anything like that, and if I have given that impression I very much hope you will give me a chance to show what a nice lot we pigfrogs really are," insisted Moundrot.

And in the weeks to come, he was as good as his word, and kept his promise to Ergo.

⁓⁎⁓

The pigfrog army had arrived back at Pigfrog Command in a very bad mood. They hadn't been very pleased about having been beaten once again by a bunch of slugs led by a fairy. Sergeant Major Pockflab had been deeply embarrassed and ashamed. He had had no knowledge of the fact that his once-feared leader was at that moment sucking up to Ergo in the most sickening fashion; that the aggression that had once formed the backbone and spirit of the pigfrog army was withering into nothing.

The remaining pigfrog commanders had issued orders for everybody to rest and recover, hoping that soon their supreme leader might somehow miraculously appear and restore their faith and courage. But as the weeks had gone by, nothing had happened. It had been on the fifth week after their ignominious defeat that Sergeant Major Pockflab had answered the phone one day at the main gate guardhouse and, to his surprise, had heard the voice of General Moundrot. It had definitely been Moundrot's voice, but somehow it hadn't seemed to be the same person. It had been like talking to somebody who was doing an impression of Moundrot. The voice had been the same, but somehow it hadn't felt quite right.

"Pockflab, my dear fellow," the voice had begun. Pockflab couldn't quite believe it.

"I've had a little bash on the head, but I'm fine now. My wife and I will soon be leaving this charming spot to return to Pigfrog Command, but I'm afraid you chaps are going to have to come down here and build Slug HQ back up again into a lovely home and barracks for our specially nice, cuddly, clever and friendly neighbours, Ergo and Elsie and everybody."

And so, unquestioningly, if a little reluctantly, the pigfrogs had obeyed. At first they had grumbled and complained to each other, but as the work progressed, they had become proud of their work, and had warmed to the task.

Having now rebuilt Slug HQ, Moundrot made a speech to the entire population of Pigfrog Command telling them they had better be nice to slugs, trolls and other creatures, and he even invited Dotty, Nige, Ergo and Elsie to dinner. Never once did he remember his days of hatred and terror. To him, and to everybody else now, he was just good old Jim Moundrot, benefactor and chief nice guy of the pigfrog nation.

—\|/—

In the years that followed, an amazing change came over the pigfrogs (even though it was less amazing than electricity, or travelling through time). Ursula insisted that every pigfrog should join the Scouts, Guides, Brownies or Cubs – which they all did with great enthusiasm, following the example of Jim Moundrot, who asked Ursula if it would be alright if he could be excused from being pack leader in case he got back into his old ways and started ordering people about. Forty-three new scout groups had to be formed to accommodate all the recruits, and the whole venture was a great success. On Thursday evenings Ursula, who was Akela to the 15th Pigfrog Group, would gather her Scouts and Cubs around her, as they all chanted "We'll Pig Dib Dib… We'll Frog Dob Dob" which meant nothing but made them feel as if they were in some sort of benevolent secret society. Each new recruit had to say the pigfrog Scout or Guide promise as he or she stood in front of the others, making the three-clawed salute, saying "I promise to do my best, to do my duty to Everybody Else, to keep the law of the pigfrog scout pack and to do a good turn to somebody every day. I also promise that as soon as I have done my good deed I shall not always wait until the next day before doing another one, should it become necessary or desirable."

A network of new roads was built in the mountains of Everywhere Else, in order to practise helping old ladies across them, although there weren't many old ladies and so that wasn't one of the best things that happened. In fact, Ursula politely ordered the roads to be turfed over again with grass, in order to help the environment.

General Jim was delighted and proud one Thursday evening to be awarded the Embroidery Badge. He had worked extremely hard on it, and frankly, he deserved it. Eventually he collected a further array of badges, including Housekeeper, Herb Gardener and Interior Decorator.

Which just goes to show that if you know anybody horrible, you should try dropping a grand piano onto them from a helicopter.

Epilogue: A Magnificent View

It was a beautiful summer's day in Don't Be So Ridiculous Valley. Ergo lay on his ramp, in his music room, playing the piano rather well, and looking out into the garden. It had been six Woodland years since he had begun the lessons, and he had learned a lot from Horace the piano elf. The soft strains of his playing filtered out through the open window into the warm afternoon air, where Elsie was preparing a picnic. She could tell that there was going to be wonderful sunset that evening.

"Go and tell Daddy that lunch is ready," she said to Rolo, her son. Rolo flew across the lawn, using his fairy wings, and landed on top of the piano.

"Mum says it's lunch time, Dad," he told Ergo.

"Thanks, Roly. I'll be there in a minute. Go and wash your slimy bits."

"OK, Dad."

Ergo thought it was good that Rolo and Lunie, his daughter, had both inherited their mother's finer points and a few of his own. Being a slug at

heart but mostly fairy was a good combination, he thought. He went out into the garden. The view was magnificent from their little wooden house right on top of the hill. You could see for about fifty Woodland miles – right out past the fish and chip trees, across I Thought I Told You Not To Be So Ridiculous Valley, down to where Dotty and Nige still lived in the lovely Tree house that dear old Jim had rebuilt for them. Then, over to the left, you could just see the edge of the Avocado Basin, and the Mauve and Avocado Mountains.

"Phew!" he thought.

"You're not wrong, there, not even a teeny little bit!" said Elsie, knowing what he was thinking, and using the sort of words that Nigel and Dotty might have used, just for fun.

"Nige and Dot will be here in a minute, Elsie," said Ergo, knowing that they had radioed over to say they would be slightly late for the picnic. No sooner had he spoken than he heard the distant whirring of the rotor blades of both Dotty and Nigel's helicopters – one pink, and one blue. They approached and landed. Dot and Nige got out, hugging Ergo and Elsie and waving to the children. Nigel gave Ergo a bottle of lemonade.

"Thanks for the lemonade," said Ergo, rather predictably.

"It was the least we could do," answered Nigel.

"Why didn't you do more then?" asked Ergo, and they all burst out laughing, remembering the words they had exchanged when Nigel's hair had caught fire, years earlier.

"It's lucky that you live right in the middle of the only valley in the world that goes upwards instead of downwards and along," observed Nigel, taking in the view and helping himself to a cheese and onion fritter.

"Absolutely," agreed Ergo.

Just then, there was a windy, blurred, swishing sound, and down, down, out of the sky, came... something. At first, Ergo was worried that it might be another grand piano. But no. Down and down it came, until they could clearly see what it was. It tumbled and rolled until it came to a stop right beside the picnic blanket. It was the Time Thimble! And out jumped Malcolms One, Two and Three – not looking a day older than they had when Ergo had last said goodbye to them during that stormy night five years before.

"Ahoy there!" they chorused to Ergo and the others.

"Time Flies!" shrieked Little Else, and ran to greet them. They hopped out.

"We know it does!" shouted the Flies.

"It's so good to see you, boys!" bubbled Elsie. "We always wondered what happened to you, and we have often thought you must have been wondering about us."

"So it all turned out alright then?" said Malcolm One.

"Oh, yes, we seem to be living happily ever after," Elsie said.

"We knew, actually," said Malcolm. "During our adventures we kept checking ahead to see what was going to happen. And by the way, we've checked the future and you do live happily ever after."

"I thought you said it was cheating to look ahead in time like that," said Ergo.

"Oh, it is," replied Malcolm One.

"We cheated!"

The End

The Mauve and Avocado Mountains

The Avocado Basin

The Incredibly Smelly River Dam

Don't Be So Ridiculous Valley

I Thought

Elftown

The Woodland Railway

This way to side of map...... ☞

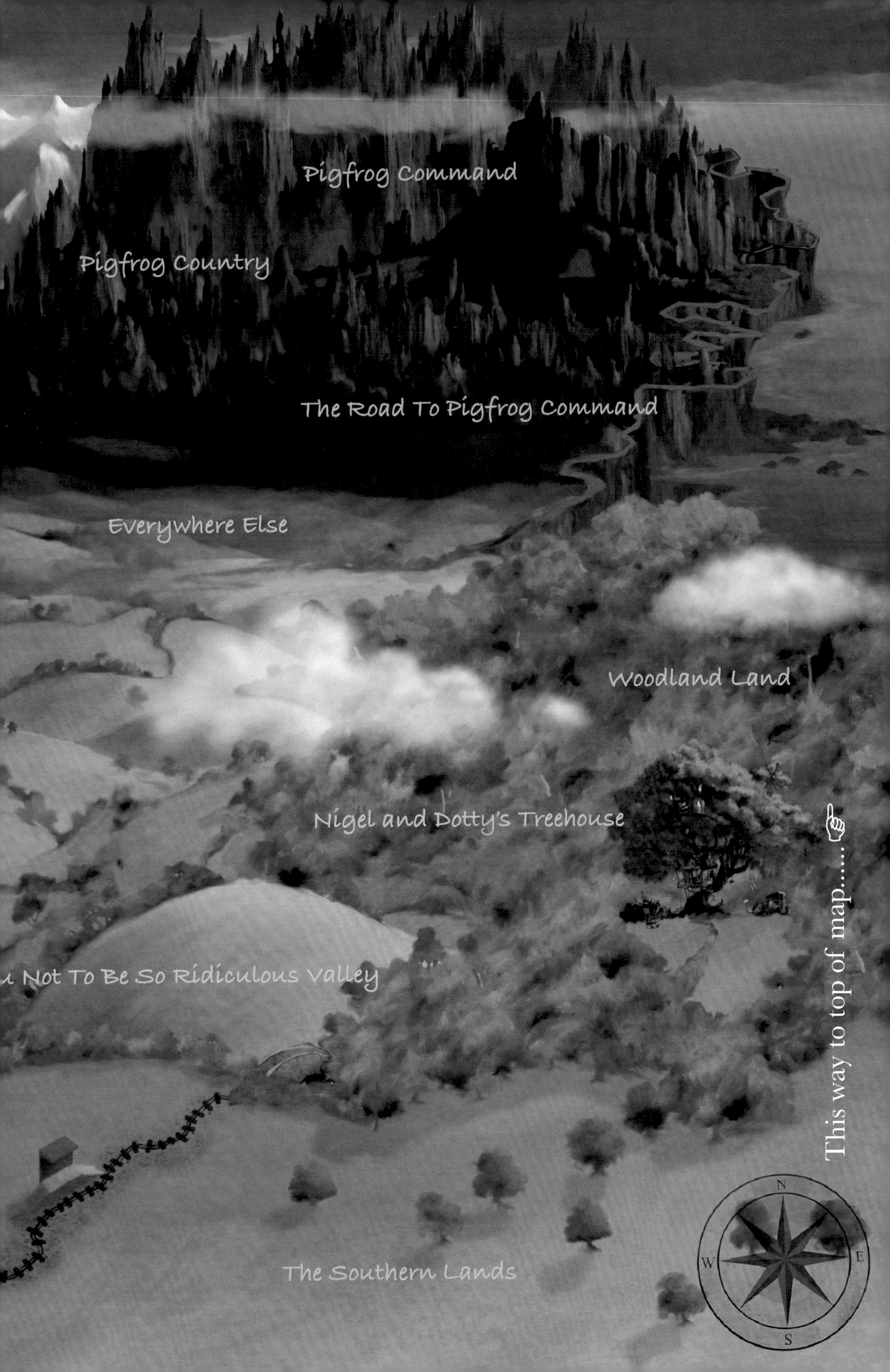

Pigfrog Command

Pigfrog Country

The Road To Pigfrog Command

Everywhere Else

Woodland Land

Nigel and Dotty's Treehouse

u Not To Be So Ridiculous Valley

The Southern Lands

This way to top of map......

N
W E
S